THE KOALA

THE KOALA

NATURAL HISTORY, CONSERVATION AND MANAGEMENT

Roger Martin & Kathrine Handasyde

Illustrations by Sue Simpson

Krieger Publishing Company
Malabar, Florida

Original Edition 1988
University of New South Wales Press

Second Edition 1999
University of New South Wales Press Ltd
and
Krieger Publishing Company
Exclusive distributor for: Americas (North, Central, & South), Caribbean, Europe, and Africa.
1725 Krieger Drive
Malabar, FL 32950-3323 USA
Tel: (407) 724-9542 Fax: (407) 951-3671
info@krieger-pub.com

FROM A DECLARATION OF PRINCIPLES JOINTLY ADOPTED BY A COMMITTEE OF THE AMERICAN BAR ASSOCIATION AND A COMMITTEE OF PUBLISHERS: This publication is designed to provide accurate and authoritative information in regard to the subject matter covered. It is sold with the understanding that the publisher is not engaged in rendering legal, accounting, or other professional service. If legal advice or other expert assistance is required, the services of a competent professional person should be sought.

Library of Congress Cataloguing-In-Publication Data:
A catalog record for this book is available from the Library of Congress, Washington, DC.

ISBN 1-57524-136-6

10 9 8 7 6 5 4 3 2

Printer Everbest Printing, Hong Kong

For Fred Baum
In memoriam

CONTENTS

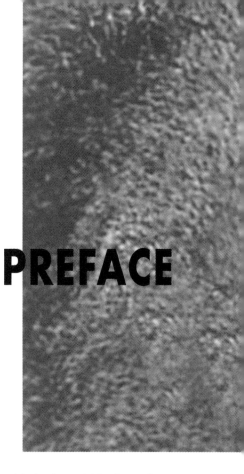

PREFACE

When the first edition of this book was published in 1988, the authors Tony Lee and Roger Martin expressed the hope that it would fill the long overdue need for a popular account of the biology of the koala. It certainly appears to have done this and, ten years on, their natural history is widely accepted as a basic reference on the subject.

New information accumulates quickly these days, and so it has with the koala. Over recent years a great deal of new research has been conducted into various aspects of their biology. It would be fair to say that in 1999 we have much deeper insights into the koala than we had ten years ago, and the discerning reader will find that the earlier volume no longer provides an adequate summary of current knowledge. This second edition has been written to redress this.

Scientific knowledge of koalas is not the only thing that has advanced over the last decade. Their status, as the icon of Australian wildlife, is now unchallenged and the general public has a seemingly insatiable appetite for news and information about koalas. This is more than a national phenomenon, as koalas are significant animals on the world stage and receive considerable attention from the international media as well. Much of this focuses on their conservation status and this is a complex issue, largely because the koala has such a broad distribution with populations occurring in a wide variety of habitats. The status of the different populations is not uniform and while some are declining, others are rapidly increasing. This has placed wildlife managers in an invidious position and while they struggle to control over-abundance in some populations, the general public believes the koala to be a rare and endangered species. An acceptable solution to the problem of over-abundance is elusive, and will remain so until the general public appreciates the nature of the problem and the consequences of doing nothing about it. Providing accessible information on the complexities of managing koalas has been a secondary factor motivating us to write this book.

While most of our first-hand experience has been within Victoria, we have striven to give an Australia-wide view of koalas (Figure P.1 shows the various localities referred to in the text), and have referred to all the studies of koalas, both published and unpublished, we could find. Information on koala populations from across the range of the species is presented. A great deal more information is available for the southern populations, as koalas are there more abundant and more accessible to researchers. Comprehensive data on populations in northern and western areas are harder to come by, largely because koalas are sparsely distributed there.

The highly abundant southern populations have offered unique opportunities to biologists interested in koalas. Where else, other than in the stunted manna gums of French Island, Victoria, could a small research team capture and examine 25 koalas in one day? Or, during management operations, gather data from more than 600 koalas from a single population. We have taken advantage of this unrivalled access to animals and some may think it has biased our view of koala ecology. While it may have, we don't think so. Ultimately, however, this is for the reader to judge.

This book is the culmination of 20 years associating with koalas, much of it spent actively researching their biology. A great many people have assisted us during this time. The original suggestion of koalas as a suitable case for a study arose from a conversation with Tony Lee sometime back in 1977. That a study program actually got off the ground, however, was largely due to the support of Bob Warneke and the late Fred Baum. Tony Lee and Ian McDonald acted as academic supervisors and, later, co-investigators in the numerous research projects subsequently carried out on koalas by both of us. Monash University was our academic home for most of this time and many people from the Departments of Zoology and Physiology contributed to the koala work. The resources of the Department of Anatomy were also occasionally tapped, and we would particularly like to thank Dan Irby, Terry Martin and Sue Simpson for their assistance. The individual research work conducted by former colleagues in the

Figure P. 1.
Places
mentioned
in the text

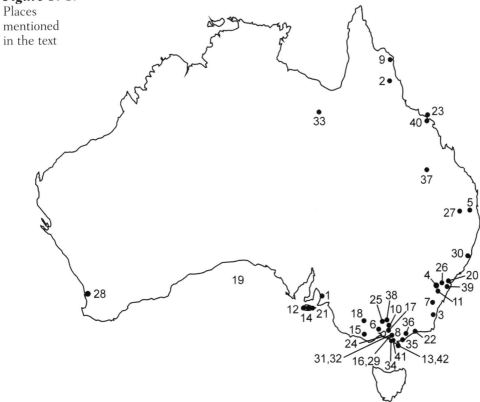

1 Adelaide	15 Framlingham	29 Phillip Island
2 Atherton Tablelands	16 French Island	30 Port Macquarie
3 Bega	17 Gembrook	31 Quail Island
4 Blue Mountains	18 Grampians National Park	32 Red Bill Creek
5 Brisbane (Moreton Bay)	19 Great Australian Bight	33 Riversleigh
6 Brisbane Ranges	20 Hawkesbury River	34 Sandy Point
7 Canberra	21 Kangaroo Island	35 Snake Island
8 Chinaman Island	22 Lake Tyers	36 South Gippsland
9 Cooktown	23 Magnetic Island	37 Springsure
10 Correnderk	24 Mornington Peninsula	38 Strathbogie Ranges
11 Cox's River	25 Nagambie	39 Sydney (Port Jackson)
12 Cygnet River	26 Nepean River	40 Townsville
13 Darby River	27 Oakey	41 Walkerville
14 Flinders Chase National Park	28 Perth	42 Wilson's Promontory

Zoology Department at Monash — particularly Peter Mitchell, Mark Hindell, Lynda Sharpe, Janet Lanyon, Lester Pahl and Keely Ough — contributed significantly to our understanding of koalas. During our Monash years we spent a great deal of time in the field and our work was made a lot easier with the help we received from the many volunteers, both Monash students and others.

Our attempts to unravel the significance of *Chlamydia* in wild koala populations in Victoria would have amounted to very little without the participation of three veterinarians: David Obendorf, Ken McColl and Laurie Gleeson. We thank them, as well as their colleagues from the former Veterinary Research Institute at Parkville, for their contribution.

Over the years wildlife officers from many regions in Victoria have supported our work. We would particularly like to acknowledge the contributions of: Percy Pullan, Mick Douglas, Stewie Scott and Allan Pullen from French Island; Jim Davidson, Kevin Brown, Charlie Nancarrow, Alan Crouch and Alan Cleeland from Phillip Island; Charlie Dickie and Mick Keenan from the Brisbane Ranges; Peter Goldstraw from Warnambool; Paul Kelly and Jim Reside from Bairnsdale; and Ross Williamson and the late Bob Austin from Yarram.

Farmers from many parts of Victoria have also been helpful, and usually very tolerant of us wandering onto their land searching for koalas. We thank them for their forbearance, and for the many koala anecdotes they shared with us. We would like to particularly thank Cec Duchier from French Island.

We would also like to thank John Seebeck and Greg Gordon for taking the time and trouble to read an earlier draft of this manuscript and for the many helpful and constructive suggestions they made. We thank Bill Foley for his comments on Chapters 4, and Andrew Krockenburger for several useful discussions on koala energy requirements. We are grateful to John Nelson for the audiogram of a koala bellow, and Bryan Dumsday for his assistance in preparing some of the illustrations for publication. We thank Peter Fell and David Paul for allowing us to use several of their photographs. We also thank Peter Menkhorst and the Victorian Department of Natural Resources and Environment and Oxford University Press for permission to use their distribution map of koalas for that State. We further thank Janet Glad, the copyright holder, for her permission to use the Norman Lindsay koala drawing and Peter Nicholson, the cartoonist of the *Australian* newspaper, for the use of his very apt summary of events on Kangaroo Island.

We acknowledge the great contribution made to this book by Sue Simpson's superb artwork. We also thank David Humfrey and his staff from Medical Illustration, Monash University.

Finally, we would like to thank the 'bears', who have maintained their sagacity and charm throughout the long association we have had with them.

Roger Martin and Kath Handasyde

KEY INFORMATION ON THE KOALA

Koala	*Phascolarctos cinereus* (GOLDFUSS 1817) Diprotodontia, Marsupialia	
Adult body weight	There is a cline in body weight from north to south, with larger animals in the south.	
	Females	**Males**
Victoria	8.5 (7–11) kg	12.0 (9.5–14.9) kg
Queensland	5.1 (4.1–7.3)	6.5 (4.2 –9.1) kg
Longevity (in wild)[1]	15+ years	12+ years
Breeding season	October–May (Most births occur between November-March)	
Gestation	35 days	
Litter size	1 (twins rare)	
Pouch life	6–8 months	
Permanently out of pouch	9 months	
Independence	12 months	
Sexual maturity	2+ years	
Sex ratio	Dependent young: 1:1[2] Independent animals: females > males (P_f 0.52–0.64)	

Notes:
1. Animals of up to 18 years have been recorded.
2. Among dependent young the sex ratio is slightly biased towards males, however this difference is not statistically significant.

CHAPTER 1

INTRODUCTION

The first, and for many years the only, book on the natural history of the koala was written by Ambrose Pratt. Entitled *The Call of the Koala*, it was published in 1937. The journalist in Pratt could not resist a pun, and his title was an ambiguous reference to both the koala's unusual vocalisations and to the charismatic hold that they then had on the popular imagination. Even today almost everyone who encounters a koala experiences this 'call'. Why is this so? Is it simply because people find them appealing to look at? Partially it is, but it is also their behaviour and the setting under which wild koalas are usually seen that makes such a lasting impression. Picture this:

> The leafy green canopy of a eucalypt forest standing highlighted against a background of midsummer blue sky. A gentle breeze, laden with the scent of the eucalypts, wafts through and sets the upper branches of the trees swaying. Suddenly, high up in the fork of a white gum, a furry grey ball catches your eye. You move, a twig cracks and the ball becomes animate. A head materialises and a face looks down at you. The animal gazes for a minute, blinks and then tucks its head down and goes back to sleep.

Both the animal and the scene touch a deep chord among Australians. Always a thing of joy to behold, the koala is the unchallenged icon of Australia, her eucalypt forests and her unique marsupial fauna.

Long before the coming of the Europeans the koala was held to be an animal of status and sagacity by the Aboriginal peoples. In contrast, the white settlers initially regarded it as sloth-like and stupid. However, this view changed and the koala's status skyrocketed, as did pride in all things Australian, following Federation at the turn of the century. The famous Australian artist Norman Lindsay was the first to cultivate the koala's potential as an Australian icon. In his cartoons Lindsay invested koalas with human personalities and through them commented on social issues and satirised public figures. On first appearance, in the *Bulletin* magazine in 1904, Lindsay's koala was nameless. However, within a few years he became the fabulous Billy Bluegum whose mission was 'to take human civilisation and culture to the barbarian bush bears' (Figure 1.1). Later he was to appear as Bunyip Bluegum in Lindsay's classic children's book *The Magic Pudding*.

Due as much to Lindsay's cartoons as to any other factor, the koala soon became entrenched in the Australian psyche. At the outset of World War I, in 1914, one of the early contingents of the First AIF to leave for Palestine took a live koala with them as a mascot. Following this war, and continuing on until the present day, the popularity of the koala has continued to grow, and its image is now widely used as a logo by commercial organisations. Open a telephone directory from any of Australia's major cities and you will find dozens of listings under 'koala'. These will include companies representing the full spectrum of commercial activity, from brass bed manufacturers to wool sellers. The image of the koala has even been embraced by a number of populist movements, including the republicans and the conservationists. Most recently, with the rise of tourism and the marketing excesses that have accompanied it, the koala has moved onto the international stage to become a symbol of all things Australian. This culminated with a very successful promotional campaign conducted by the Australian international airline Qantas in the United States of America. The Qantas campaign made a television star out of a surprisingly loquacious koala that climbed around one of their aircraft extolling the virtues of holidaying in Australia.

The koala had very powerful antecedents in all of this. Edward, or 'Teddy', Bear was a universally popular soft toy in the Western world. For many of us it was our first bedtime companion. AA Milne's

Figure 1.1
This very human koala first appeared in 1912 in a series of drawings by Norman Lindsay. It illustrates the impact that Billy Bluegum's introduction of human civilisation and culture had on the barbarian bush bears. (Reprinted with permission from the copyright holder, Janet Glad.)

'Winnie the Pooh' capitalised on Edward's popularity to become one of the favourite books of everyone's childhood. Some have suggested that this 'teddy bear syndrome' is even more deeply seated in the human psyche. Some years ago Ronald Strahan of the Australian Museum pointed out that as the koala had neither tail nor snout and with eyes that looked forward rather than to the side, it was in fact very humanoid. Borrowing from the jargon of ethnology (the science of animal behaviour developed by Konrad Lorenz and Nikko Tinbergen), Strahan argued that its physical appearance acted as an 'innate releasing mechanism' for human affection.

Extending Strahan's thesis, the relatively large head size and the overall head to body proportions of a koala resemble those of a young child. When in its normal sitting position, on its rump with its hind legs tucked up, this head to body ratio for a koala is about 1:3 (Figure 1.2). This is a similar to that displayed by 12 to 18-month-old human babies, who also spend a lot of time sitting on their rumps with their legs tucked up. Human babies elicit (or release) a strong maternal response and their head to body proportions are part of the stimulus. They are effectively signalling to receptive adults that they are young and helpless and in need of love and protection. Recall the label that was permanently attached to Paddington, that other bear of childhood: 'Please look after this bear. Thank you.' To many people, wild koalas are effectively carrying the same message.

In the first paragraph we tried to recreate the circumstances under which many people have had their first encounter with a wild koala. It is a memorable event and, depending on the perspective of

Figure 1.2
The similar head-to-body proportions of an adult koala and an 18-month old child may be part of the reason why koalas provoke a strong maternal response in humans.

the viewer, evokes a range of emotions. Before the arrival of Europeans over two hundred years ago, such an encounter would have been of special significance to an Aboriginal Australian. Koalas were eminent animals and respected for their sagacity in the mythology of many tribes. The indigenous hunter may have spent a while in communion with the animal before moving on. However, if the laws of his tribe permitted it and he was hungry, he might kill and eat the animal. The flesh of koalas was savoured by the indigenous Australians.

For modern-day Australians, the vast majority of whom are urban dwellers living on the eastern seaboard of the continent, an encounter with a wild koala is still a special event. It is both elating and reassuring to see one, especially at a time when they are widely believed to be a rare and vulnerable species. Foreign tourists are also enchanted and many regard such a sighting as the highlight of their visit. For some Australians however, particularly farmers living in the south-east corner of the continent, seeing a koala gives rise to mixed emotions. Like anyone else, rural people find it hard to resist the koala's charisma but they know that coexisting with these 'tree-eaters' is not easy. Many landholders face a continuous struggle to prevent koalas from over-browsing and killing the remnant old eucalyptus trees around their farms.

Whatever the perspective of the viewer, the koala remains an extraordinarily attractive animal. In Ambrose Pratt's words: 'No more gentle, harmless, trustful, quaintly comical, wistfully curious, wise looking, pathetic and lovable little creature ever existed'. The power of its charisma has made the koala an international symbol of the beauty and vulnerability of wildlife. It fulfils this role admirably but one of the problems of dealing with an animal species once it becomes an icon is that we tend to lose track of the basic facts of its biology. For a number of reasons, not the least being the difficult issue of over-abundance in some koala populations, it is important that we do not do this.

WHAT IS A KOALA?

We have described how different people perceive it, but what exactly is a koala? Zoologists would describe it as a medium-sized mammal belonging to the group known as the Marsupialia (the marsupials). One key characteristic of marsupials is that the females give birth, after a very short gestation, to young that are tiny, hairless and blind. The miracle of such a birth is that the young, after emerging from the birth canal in this virtually embryonic condition, climb the fur of their mother's belly unaided, find and enter the pouch then attach to a teat where they continue their growth and development.

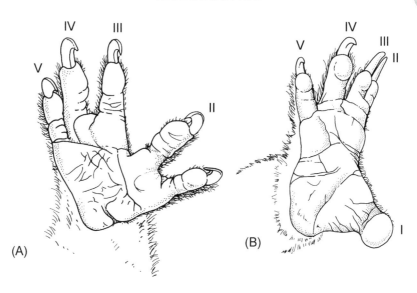

Figure 1.3
The right forepaw (*manus*: A) and hind paw (*pes: B*) of the koala. The forepaw is relatively large with the first and second digits opposed to the third, fourth and fifth. This conformation, known as a 'forcipate' hand, is thought to be an adaptation for grasping small branches. The strongly curved claws attached to most digits are, in the main, also used for climbing. The second and third digits of the hind paw are fused together and the claws attached to them are used more as a comb for grooming. This fused state, known as 'syndactyl', is one of the distinguishing characteristics of marsupials in the Order Diprotodonta.

Zoologists subdivide the marsupials into four major groups, or Orders. The koala is a member of the Order Diprotodontia. Diprotodontids have two distinguishing characteristics: they have only one functional pair of incisors in their lower jaw; and the second and third toes on their hind feet are fused together in a state known as syndactyl (see Figure 1.3). Other members of this Order are kangaroos, possums and wombats. The koala is distantly related to the wombats (see Figure 1.4) and the Families to which they belong, the Phascolarctidae and the Vombatidae, are grouped together into the same Sub-order, the Vombatiformes. The koala is the only surviving member of the Family Phascolarctidae.

Members of a Family are further classified into individual species using a binomial system which allocates them to a Genus and species. The name given to the koala is *Phascolarctos cinereus*. The generic name, given by the French taxonomist Henri de Blainville in 1816, is derived from two Greek words, 'phaskolos' meaning pouch and 'arktos' meaning bear. The second part of the name 'cinereus', meaning ashy or ash-coloured, was given the following year by the German taxonomist Goldfuss. Hence, in the scientific literature, the koala's name is often given as *Phascolarctos cinereus* (GOLDFUSS 1817).

That is how they are classified zoologically, but what exactly is a koala? In essence, it is a medium-sized, slow-moving mammal possessing a suite of characteristics that enable it to live in trees and feed on foliage. Many of these characteristics could be regarded as 'adaptations' for this lifestyle. The extremely sharp claws and very powerful upper body, essential climbing equipment when confronted with smooth-barked eucalypts, are examples. Collectively, these adaptations have resulted in the koala having a stocky body and this, combined with rounded ears, thick fur and the lack of a tail, gives it a bear-like appearance. This prompted the koala's scientific name and underlies its widespread public appeal.

VARIATION IN THE TYPES OF KOALAS

The Koala occurs across a very wide geographic range that encompasses many different climates, substrates, forest types and food supplies. Koalas have a long evolutionary history and local populations have had adequate time to adapt to local conditions. These adaptations, particularly the differences in body size, and pelage (fur) density and colour, were recognised by the early taxonomists who described three different 'races' or sub-species of the koala (Table 1.1).

Figure 1.4
A common wombat (*Vombatus ursinus*). Wombats are the koala's closest living marsupial relatives. (Barbara Triggs)

Table 1.1

The races of the koala (*Phascolarctos cinereus*)

Race or sub-species	Distribution	Described by	Year described
P. cinereus cinereus	intermediate	Goldfuss	1817
P. cinereus adjustus	northern	Oldfied Thomas	1923
P. cinereus victor	southern	Ellis Troughton	1935

The type specimen (the first koala described by taxonomists) came from the Nepean River area of New South Wales. The German taxonomist Goldfuss gave this type specimen the specific name *cinereus* because of the ashy tips of the fur that gave it a 'mixed grey colour'. Oldfield Thomas later described a second race, *adjustus* , based on a Queensland specimen, largely because animals from the north were much smaller and had a very short coat compared to their hirsute cousins from the south. This is particularly noticeable if you compare animals from the extremes of the koalas range, from the far north of Queensland with southern Victoria (see Plates 1a and 1b). The animals from the north are around half the body weight (for males about 6 kilograms compared to 12 kilograms) and tend to have short, silver-grey fur. It was the large size (adult males occasionally weigh in excess of 14 kilograms), longer thicker coat and more cinnamon-coloured fur that caused Ellis Troughton to assign the southern animals to a third race, *victor*. These differences could all be ascribed to the radically different climatic conditions that koalas experience at the extremes of their very broad range.

THE NEED FOR A NATURAL HISTORY OF KOALAS

Encounters with wildlife elicit a range of responses. In the main they stimulate curiosity. What is it? Where does it live? What does it eat? Is it a male or a female? How many young does it have? How long does it live? What is it related to? Is it endangered? Like those of a five-year-old child, the questions are endless. Some people seek information about wildlife because they are students, studying courses which deal with issues involving wildlife or conservation. For others it is simply to improve their knowledge of native fauna, and add to their understanding and appreciation of the bush. Others still seek to enhance their relationship with wild creatures for more deep seated, even spiritual, reasons. So where does this diverse group of people get their information?

In bygone centuries, when the natural sciences were more the province of wealthy amateurs and under-employed clerics, natural histories of species were the norm. If you could read and afford to buy books, information on wild creatures was relatively accessible, even if not always accurate. In the early decades of this century most newspapers featured a natural history column and in this way much information about wildlife was disseminated to the general public. Many of the writers of these pieces were associated with zoos or wildlife parks and some were even academic zoologists. Over recent decades, however, increasing specialisation and the rise of professionalism has resulted in a diaspora of the natural scientists. Once broad disciplines have been subdivided into a multitude of narrow specialities populated by experts who more often than not find each other incomprehensible. Much detailed information about wildlife is gathered and published but most of it is in scientific journals that are relatively inaccessible to lay people. Even if this information was more available, the reports are written for an audience of scientists and often address highly esoteric questions. There is an increasing amount of natural history information available on the electronic media and while some of it is excellent, it has its constraints. For these reasons written natural histories still have an important role to play. The ideal natural history should be a plainly written narrative that integrates pertinent historical information about a species with the most up-to-date scientific facts of its biology. Most importantly, particularly for a charismatic species like the koala, it should examine the question of cultural context and, if successful, influence it.

This has been kept in mind for this natural history of the koala. It begins with an overview that draws on sources as far flung as the fossil record and folk history, and even includes some mythological history of koalas passed down by oral tradition among indigenous Australians. Many will find these myths delightful, but they are also insightful and particularly pertinent at this time.

The present day distribution and abundance of koalas is very pertinent when assessing their conservation status, and the latest information on this is also presented. Where koalas occur is dictated by a number of factors, with the presence of preferred food being one of the most significant. The ability of koalas to survive on eucalypt leaf, which is unpalatable and potentially toxic to most animals, depends on a complex set of behavioural, anatomical and physiological adaptations, and these are discussed at some length.

This natural history also includes a synthesis of the latest information on the behaviour, sociality and life cycle of koalas. This is followed by a lengthy discussion of koala population biology, a topic which is poorly understood by both scientists and the general public alike. The significance of diseases, particularly those caused by *Chlamydia*, is also widely misunderstood, and these are dealt with in some detail. The apparent paradox of simultaneously having koala populations declining in some areas while over-abundant and killing their food-trees in others is related to their chlamydial infection status and this is demonstrated in a series of case histories. The book concludes with a discussion of the major conservation and management issues that face the koala today.

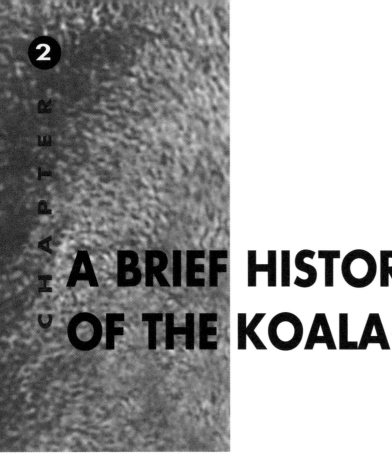

A BRIEF HISTORY OF THE KOALA

The history of a species over geological time is called its 'evolutionary history' and the area of science which studies animals over this time frame is known as 'palaeontology'. Palaeontologists look at the lineage of species and from these hypothesise on the evolutionary processes and environments which have acted to produce the animals seen today. Their work relies almost exclusively on the fossil record and for any one species this is often a very sparse record. This was true for koalas and views on their evolutionary history were somewhat tentative. Over the last decade, however, a large amount of fossil koala material has been unearthed and with this new material a more confident view of the evolutionary history of koalas has emerged.

EVOLUTIONARY HISTORY: FROM RAIN-FOREST TO EUCALYPT WOODLAND

Koalas and their immediate ancestors have been around for a very long time, at least 25 million years. The consensus among palaeontologists is that the koala lineage arose from a Diprotodont ancestor some time back in the early Oligocene Era (35 million years ago or 35 mya). Diprotodonts are now extinct, but were a group of giant marsupials, believed to be somewhat similar in appearance to very

Figure 2.1
These drawings of teeth illustrate the gross similarity of molars from a Miocene koala, *Perikoala robustus*, (partial jaw only) and a modern koala, *Phascolarctos cinereus*.

large wombats. The largest are estimated to have weighed around 2 tonnes.

The earliest koala-like animals are known from the Late Oligocene (25 mya) and Middle Miocene (15 mya) and three genera have been described from this early period. These are *Litokoala*, *Madakoala* and *Perikoala*. Another two genera, *Koobor* and the still surviving *Phascolarctos*, have been described from the later Pliocene (4.5 to 2 mya). All of these genera were distinguished as koalas on the basis of the morphology of their teeth. The structures of these teeth are broadly similar in all of the material examined (see Figure 2.1), and this is interpreted to mean that, size differences apart, Oligo-Miocene koalas were very similar to the Pliocene animals and to the extant species, *Phascolarctos cinereus*.

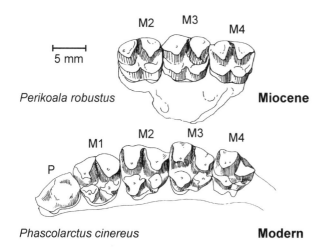

5 mm

M2 M3 M4

Perikoala robustus **Miocene**

M1 M2 M3 M4

P

Phascolarctus cinereus **Modern**

A great deal more fossil material from koalas has been discovered over the last two decades, enabling this view of their evolutionary history to be further developed and refined. This new material has come to light largely because of the efforts of palaeontologist Michael Archer and his colleagues from the University of New South Wales. Their work has focussed on a fossil deposit at Riversleigh in central Queensland. Over the years Riversleigh has yielded a vast amount of material from a large number of species, all belonging to what is believed to have been an ancient rainforest fauna. The quantity and diversity of this material has allowed Archer and his colleagues to draw two very interesting conclusions about koalas. Firstly, based on the relatively small number of koala fossils compared to the huge amount of material found from other groups, they suggest that koalas were in low abundance in these ancient forests. Secondly, based on similarities in the shape and structure of the teeth of the ancient and modern koalas, they suggest that they probably both ate a similar diet.

Gut contents are normally not preserved and there is no information on the diet of Oligo-Miocene koalas. Present-day koalas rely almost entirely on the foliage of trees from the Genus *Eucalyptus* for food (as discussed fully in Chapter 4) and palaeobotanists believe that the ancestors of modern eucalypts occurred in the Oligo-Miocene rainforest. Again, there is no information on how abundant they were, but based on their restricted distribution in rainforests of the present day the presumption is that they were sparse. Archer and his colleagues have speculated that the apparently low abundance of koalas in these ancient rainforests may have been because they relied on a relatively uncommon food resource: the foliage of these ancestral eucalypts.

The rise of the eucalypts in Australia began with the onset of drier climates in the late Tertiary Period (5 mya). In northern Australia these drier conditions favoured the spread of eucalypt-dominated woodlands at the expense of rainforest. Archer and his colleagues reason that if koalas were already reliant on eucalypt foliage as their main food, the spread of eucalypts would have increased the food resources available to them and thus allowed them also to increase their distribution and abundance. They go on to suggest that this continuing trend towards drier climates in Australia spelt doom for koala populations in some areas.

The localities of fossil finds indicate that koalas were once widely distributed across the south and east of the Australian continent (Figure 2.2). Remains of the modern koala, *Phascolarctos*, have been found in late-Pleistocene (30,000 years ago) cave deposits both north and south of Perth, Western Australia, as well as from caves further east, on the southern edge of the Nullarbor Plain. These areas are now well outside the koala's range, and Archer and his colleagues attribute these local extinctions to the dry climates and radical environmental changes of the late-Pleistocene. However, during the same period koalas also disappeared from the wetter, south-western corner of Western Australia and Archer's group finds it difficult to attribute this extinction to the same environmental cause. Instead they suggest it might be related to the arrival of Aboriginal people.

THE IMPACT OF EARLY MAN

Recent estimates, based on evidence from a number of sources, suggest a human presence in Australia from somewhere between 60,000 and 120,000 years ago. A number of the larger marsupials (the Australian megafauna) went to extinction over this period and there is a school of thought among palaeontologists that the hunting activities of early humans contributed to this. Recent discoveries at a 30,000-year-old fossil site, at Cuddie Springs in New South Wales, have added weight to this hypothesis. At this site the bones of large, now extinct marsupials were found together with blood-stained stone tools, charcoal and other signs of human activity.

The relative impacts of hunting and of climatic change on the

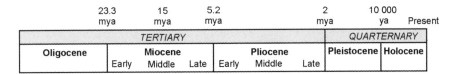

23.3 mya	15 mya	5.2 mya	2 mya	10 000 ya	Present
TERTIARY				QUARTERNARY	
Oligocene	Miocene	Pliocene	Pleistocene	Holocene	
	Early · Middle · Late	Early · Middle · Late			

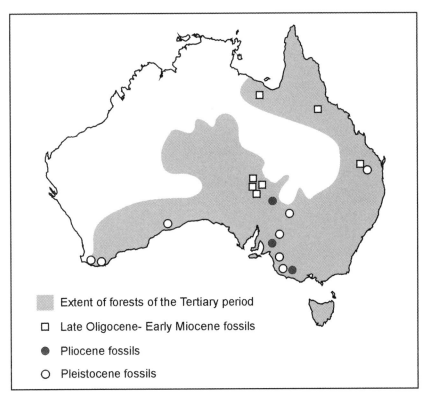

Extent of forests of the Tertiary period

□ Late Oligocene- Early Miocene fossils

● Pliocene fossils

○ Pleistocene fossils

Figure 2.2
Koala fossil localities coincide with what is thought to be the distribution of rainforests during the Tertiary Period. The distribution of the forest is based on the occurrence of pollen from the rainforest genus *Nothofagus* in the fossil record.

viability of the Australian megafauna is a contentious topic of academic debate, and it will remain so until more evidence becomes available. However, hypotheses on what has happened in the distant past are always difficult to resolve. The only evidence is in the fossil record and this is patchy and subject to a range of interpretations. Despite this, there is no doubt that human activities — burning practices as well as hunting — would have had a significant impact on the abundance of large and medium sized mammals in Australia, and may have contributed to the extinction of some. During the driest period of the Pleistocene there was probably only a relatively small area of habitat suitable for koalas left in the south-west and it is plausible that this remnant population was hunted or burned to extinction.

There is no doubt that the indigenous Australians were skilled hunters and that koalas were highly valued game animals to them. There are many eye-witness accounts that attest to this. One of the most convincing is given by John Bulmer, a Christian missionary who lived with the remnants of the Gippsland tribes at Lake Tyers, Victoria, in the late nineteenth century. In describing their economy, Bulmer observed that the Gippsland Aborigines:

> ... also fed on the flesh of the native bear or sloth [koala]. They used their tomahawks to cut notches in the bark, which they use as toe holds to climb very high, straight trees. Sometimes they used a band made of stringy bark (yangoro) which encircled the tree and their bodies. This made it easier to cut the notches.
>
> The plan was for one man to climb up the tree and the other waited on the ground. After much labour they got to the top of the tree, sometimes a very giddy height, but they were perfectly cool and proceeded to kill their game. It often happened that the bear would get on to a very remote bough, when it had to be cut to let the animal fall, but there would be others below to dispatch it. After all their labour I have seen the bear leap onto another tree, when they must begin their work again or leave it. They generally did the latter.
>
> It was pitiable to hear the very mournful sound the bear made when in danger, it was almost human. I think a tender hearted man would have let the animal have its life, but hunger makes men overlook all else.
>
> I must say Gippslanders were the most daring tree climbers, as they seemed to be quite at home on the top. They were willing to take risks to get their food. As a rule I think they had always a good supply.

Bulmer's account is testament to the skill and persistence of the hunters. Whether their activity had the potential to significantly effect the abundance of koalas or to eliminate them from some areas entirely is a more difficult question to resolve but we will return to this again later.

MYTHOLOGICAL HISTORY

This relationship between koalas and indigenous hunters leads us to another source of information and another type of history. This history comes from the time before the arrival of the Europeans in Australia and therefore relies on a 'quasi-historical' record. Largely it is in the form of myths and stories but it is the only record we have of the knowledge of these hunters, the knowledge of the Aboriginal people.

In hunter-gatherer societies, stories featuring the most favoured game animals are incorporated into the mythology of the tribe. These stories are retold from generation to generation and become, over time, a mixture of biological fact, myth, magico-religious practice and tribal custom. Much of the oral tradition of the Aboriginal people has been lost during their recent tragic history but a number of their stories featuring koalas have survived. These are both delightful and insightful, revealing as they do a view of the species that was both spiritual and utilitarian. The beliefs and practices of a culture that lived in ecological balance with koalas for tens of thousands of years are also important because they put the difficult problems of koala management (discussed in Chapter 8) in a broader context.

This first story, recorded by Roland Robinson, was told by a Ngumbarr man from Port Macquarie on the north coast of New South Wales.

THE FLOOD

One time all the land in the world was joined up in one big country. The big flood came and the world was covered. As the water began to go down, the streams and currents of water divided the land up into islands.

There was some people left on one of these islands. It might have been that country called Africa. These people were cut off, living on that island. Those people were great throwers of the boomerang. They could split a tree with the boomerang. They could throw their boomerangs into the sky until they went out of sight. They were hard throwers in those times.

One man was throwing his boomerang in that country. He threw it hard and far. It travelled into the sky, away out of sight. The boomerang flew and hit a tree in the country of Australia. That tree was near the beach at Middle Head, down from Macksville.

'Oh,' those people on the island cried. 'There's land over there.' But they didn't know how to get back to this country.

Then a little boy started to cry. He was crying and crying and crying. All his people tried to give him witchetty grub, honey, paddymelon, carpet snake, wallaby. All kinds of tucker they bought to him. But the little boy would take that tucker and throw it away and go on crying and crying.

The little boy's brother-in-law, Ngudgeegullum, came along. He bought him a 'dungirr', a koala bear. He said to the boy, 'Do you want this?'

'Ngee!' said the little boy.

The brother-in-law took the bear and killed it. He opened it up and took out the guts. Then he took the intestines and threw them at the little boy and hit him in the stomach with them.

'Yarree, jagurr, yarngoo yarri,' said the little boy. 'I'm going down to the beach now.' He took the koala bear's intestines down to the beach and started to blow them up with his mouth.

'Yes, that's right,' said his brother-in-law. The little boy started to laugh then.

Those intestines started to go right up into the sky. The little boy blew into them, 'boombi' we call them. They began to curve over the sky and make a bridge.

All those people, those tribes on the island, started to walk across on that bridge. Ngudgeegullum, the brother-in-law, went first and the little boy followed him. As they walked across the bridge, Ngudgeegullum kept saying, 'I'll cut it off now! I'll cut it off!' He wanted to cut the bridge with his stone axe.

But the little boy said, 'Don't do that! Wait until we are all over there.'

When all the people landed on the beach at Middle Head — that's where the bridge ended when it went across the sky — Ngudgeegullum cut it off with his stone tomahawk. 'Now,' he said, 'you can float away. I don't want to see you any more. Now you can turn into a rainbow.' So the bridge turned into a rainbow and floated away.

There was no sea at that time. It was just calm water. 'Now,' said Ngudgeegullum to the water, 'you've got to chase me now.' The water started to roll. It started to roll into the beach in big waves. Ngudgeegullum ran up and down the beach crying out, 'Come on! Chase me!' The water, it rolled and it rolled, trying to chase Ngudgeegullum. That's how the sea started. That's how it is today.

'Now,' said Ngudgeegullum to the little boy, 'you must turn into the koala bear and I must turn into the native cat. Our names are dungirr and barnjull.' So these two turned into the koala bear and native cat.

Then all those people who landed at that place split up into different tribes. They went to different rivers. That's why the tribes talk different languages all over Australia.

This story has overtones of both Gondwana and Genesis, and suggests that the relationship between koalas and the Aboriginal people goes back a very long way. It also underlines the koalas status as a game animal and, in doing so, highlights the anatomical fact that koalas have an extremely long gut. (Their gut also impressed the nineteenth-century English anatomist Richard Owen who described the caecum as being of 'enormous magnitude'.)

Another story from the north coast of New South Wales, again recorded by Robinson, relates how the old people of the Githavul tribe used to go back into the hills to visit a site where a particularly large stone stood prominently out of the hillside. This was a 'story place', a site sacred to the 'boorabee' (koala), and the old people used to go there and chant songs of increase: 'Gumbee wanjin boorabee (Make plenty of bears)'.

William Thomas was a Protector of Aborigines in Victoria between 1839 and 1849 and a sympathetic recorder of the myths of the southern tribes. Many of these were later cited by R Brough Smyth in his 1878 publication *The Aborigines of Victoria* from which the following excerpt comes.

> The Native Bear, *Kur-bo-roo*, is the sage counsellor of the Aborigines in all their difficulties. When bent on a dangerous expedition, the men will seek help from this clumsy creature, but in what way his opinions are made known is nowhere recorded. He is revered if not held sacred. The Aborigines may eat him, but they may not skin him as they skin the kangaroo and the opossum. A long time ago Kur-bo-roo stole all the drinking vessels (*Tarnuk*) belonging to the Aborigines, and he drained the creeks and made such a scarcity of water that all the women and young children cried aloud. The men, women and children had no water to drink; Kur-bo-roo had taken it all. Much distressed and perplexed, the Aborigines gave way at length to extreme despair, for no help came to them. Kur-ruk-ar-ook seeing all these things, came down from the sky, and inquired into the causes of this sorrow. Kur-ruk-ar-ook called all the bears to her and heard their complaints, and she heard also all that the Aborigines had to say and she settled the quarrel thus:
>
> The blacks might eat the flesh of the bear, because it was good, but they might not skin it as they skinned common animals; and the bears were commanded not to steal the Tarnuk or the waters of the creek; and all of them, blacks and bears, became friends by means of the counsel given by Kur-ruk-ar-ook. Thenceforth the bear became well disposed towards the blacks, and ever ready to give advice and help to them.

The koala was known as 'Koob-boor' to the Upper Yarra tribes and their version of this myth gave more detail on how the koala should be treated before it was eaten and the consequences for the tribe if this law was broken.

From this time Koob-boor became food for the people; but it is a law amongst the people that they must not break his bones when they kill him, neither take off his skin before they roast him. If the law were broken, Koob-boor would again become powerful, and he would dry up the waters of the creeks. Koob-boor always keeps near the banks of the creeks, and near water holes, so if the law be broken he may at once carry away the water.

William Thomas had personal experience of just how strongly the Aboriginal people adhered to this belief when he was superintendent of the mission station at Correnderk, near Healesville. He wrote:

I sadly wanted a bear's skin to make a cap, but I could never get it. One day a man of the Yarra tribe, who had bought in a bear early, before the rest of the blacks had returned to the encampment, was importuned by me to skin it. He refused to skin it; but, at length, by giving him presents, and showing him that no harm could come of the act, because all the sorcerers and all the blacks who could communicate with the sorcerers and other chief men were absent, he took off the skin and gave it to me. I took the skin to my tent and meant to make it into a cap, but the young man became very restless. Remorse overtook him. He could not put the skin on again, nor indeed, had he wished to do so, would I have given it up. He said, 'Poor blacks lose 'em all water now,' and he became so much alarmed, and exhibited such contrition and terror, that the old doctors came to inquire into the cause. He told all. Much excitement followed. I said that the blacks had nothing to fear. I laughed at their terrors; but at length I was obliged to give them the skin. The skin and the bear were buried in the same manner in which a black man is buried. Though the bear was actually roasting, his body was taken away and buried with the skin. This ceremony they all believed would propitiate the bears and avert the calamity of a loss of water.

Thomas related another incident which confirms that 'Kur-bo-roo' also kept his part of the agreement.

The bear is a privileged animal, and is often consulted in very great under-takings. I was once out with a celebrated Westernport black, tracking five other blacks. The tracks had been lost for some days at a part of the country where we expected they must pass. We ran down a creek; after going some miles, a bear made a noise as we passed. The black stopped and a parley commenced. I stood gazing alternately at the black and the bear. At length my black came to me and said: 'The big one stupid: bear tell me you no go that way.' We immediately crossed the creek and took a different way. Strange as it may appear, we had not altered our course above a mile and a half before we came upon the tracks and never lost them after.

Descendants of the Girae Wurrung people still live at Framlingham, in Western Victoria, and they tell their children a different type of koala story, to caution them on the dangers of indolence. It was recorded by Ange Broeders.

Long time ago, in the time of our dreaming, there was a man whose name was Wun'gill. He was a very lazy man. His wife, Warron (bandicoot), was left to do all the work, even hunting for food, so her family would not starve. One day Warron's brother, Kurrin, came to talk to Wun'gill and told him: 'We are going hunting today, I think it will be a good day to hunt.'

But Wun'gill said: 'It will be too warm today. I think I'll rest under a tree instead.'

Soon the whole tribe became tired of Wun'gill's laziness. He wouldn't do anything to help anyone. Even the animals learnt that they could walk right by Wun'gill and he'd be too lazy to even try to catch them for food.

Warron became so fed up that she began calling to the great spirit, Bunjil, for help. 'What can I do great spirit, my husband is too lazy to help me?'

All of the tribe began to continually ask Wun'gill for advice, to see if a feeling of importance would rid him of his laziness. Soon Wun'gill got sick of people asking him to help them hunt, or make spears or perform Karweean (cooorobooree). So one day he decided to hide from everyone. He searched everywhere and finally found the biggest manna gum in the bush.

'No one will bother me up there,' he thought, so he climbed right up to the top. It was the most work he'd done all his life and he immediately fell asleep.

Little did he know that, after hearing Warron's cry for help, the great spirit Bunjil (wedge-tailed eagle) had been keeping an eye on him. Bunjil now watched with great interest. He saw Wun'gill sleep all day and night and make no effort to look for food or water. For three days Wun'gill slept and on the fourth day Bunjil decided to weave some magic. Bungill took the form of Bon-bon-taer-ae-mot (black cockatoo) and called to Wun'gill:

'Arrk, arrk, eat the gum leaf and you'll never have to work again.'

Then he flew off, singing a strange song:

'Tukka-wan Taerang Deen-gniitch Laenann.'

Wun'gill thought about what the black cockatoo had told him. It sounded like a great idea and so he ate a gum leaf but couldn't decide whether he liked it or not so he tried another one, and then another. Soon Bunjil's magic began to work and Wun'gill started to change. His arms and legs grew shorter, the nails of his fingers and toes became claws and he grew fur all over his body. He turned into a koala!

So now we know why the koala is lazy. Like their father, all of Wun'gill's children were lazy too and they all became koalas who just ate gum leaves and then slept all day. And take care if you sit around all day doing nothing for Bunjil might weave his magic on you or Wun'gill might even come for you himself.

'Tukka-wan Taerang Deen-gniitch Laenann.'

RECENT HISTORY

The recent history of the koala is that recorded by Europeans since their settlement in Australia over two hundred years ago. Compared with the time scales of both evolutionary history and Aboriginal habitation of Australia, this is an infinitesimally short period of time. Yet it has been a time of major change for koala populations, as many of the practices followed by Europeans, particularly their wide-scale clearing of native forest, have had a severe impact.

FIRST CONTACT: KOALA ABUNDANCE AT THE TIME OF EUROPEAN SETTLEMENT

It was not until 1798, ten years after the establishment of the English penal settlement at Port Jackson in Sydney Cove, that John Price, a servant of the Governor of the colony, first reported the existence of a sloth-like creature that the local Aboriginals called 'cullawine'. This sighting took place in the Blue Mountains, about 90 kilometres southwest of Sydney. It was the first inkling white settlers had that the Australian bush harboured such a creature.

Four years later, in 1802, Francis Barrallier, an aide-de-camp of Governor King, collected the first material evidence. Barrallier was in the bush some distance from Sydney when his party met up with a group of Aboriginal hunters who had recently captured a 'monkey' which they knew as 'colo'. The animal had already been butchered but Barrallier salvaged what he could as a zoological specimen. He only succeeded in obtaining the paws for which his black assistant, Gory, had to trade two spears and a tomahawk. (Given the utility of a steel tomahawk, the paws of the animal were obviously of some value to the hunters.) Barrallier preserved the paws in a bottle of brandy and duly presented them to the Governor. It was not until the following year, the fourteenth after the establishment of the colony, that the first live koala was bought into Sydney.

Early records such as these give the impression that koalas weren't particularly abundant in the countryside surrounding Sydney in the early years of settlement. Things may have changed by 1836 when surveyor William Govatt reported that koalas 'were numerous on the ranges leading to Cox's River, below the mountain precipes, and also in the ravines which open into the Hawkesbury River, as well as in various other parts of the colony'.

However John Gould, mammal collector and author of the *Mammals of Australia*, did not find this to be the case in either the mountain or coastal forests to the north of the settlement. Gould traversed the region between Sydney and Moreton Bay (Brisbane) between 1838 and 1840, collecting mammal specimens. He reported that it was only with the assistance of keen-eyed Aborigines that he was able to find any koalas at all. He found them to be present in all localities but they were nowhere abundant and always difficult to obtain. He was pessimistic about their chances of survival, predicting them 'certain to become gradually more scarce and to be ultimately extirpated'.

In 1844, further to the south, a party led by the Polish explorer Paul Strzelecki encountered koalas during their exploratory traverse of eastern Victoria. The last two weeks of their trip was through the tall, wet eucalypt forests of South Gippsland and during this time they relied on koala as their only food. Riley, one of the party, later recorded:

> we only saw one animal through the country we passed, the size of a small dog, which lives in trees — a monkey or native bear. We got some by shooting, some by the natives climbing the trees. We ate them raw when we could not make a fire which was difficult because dry fuel was scarce.

While it kept them alive Strzelecki and his party apparently did not relish the experience and, in their later correspondence, made jocular reference to each other as the 'bear eaters'.

CHANGES IN KOALA ABUNDANCE FOLLOWING THE DECLINE OF THE ABORIGINES

Contrary to Gould's prediction, koalas were abundant in many areas of southern Australia by the middle years of the nineteenth century. George Augustus Robinson, the Chief Protector of Aborigines in the Port Phillip district, was the first to comment on this and attribute a cause. On a journey through South Gippsland in 1844, Robinson suggested that many of the forest animals, particularly koalas and lyrebirds, had increased vastly since the decline of the local Aboriginal tribes.

Similarly in the Bega district in southern New South Wales, old records note that koala numbers increased markedly following white settlement in the early years of the nineteenth century. By 1865 it was possible to catch one in the main street of Bega. Perhaps significantly, in the census returns for the period 1841 and 1845, only 160 Aboriginal people were known to be alive in the Monaro District (which includes Bega). By 1871 this number had shrunk to 33.

The apparently inverse relationship between the local abundance of koalas and the status of the remnant Aboriginal tribes was also noted by Fred Parris in Victoria. As an amateur historian Parris became curious about the changing abundance of koalas during the period of his family's stewardship of an area of rich river flats on the Goulburn River, near Nagambie in central Victoria. His forebears had settled the area in the 1870s. Relying on the published accounts of explorers who had visited the area prior to this time, as well as the early diaries of his family, Parris reconstructed the history of the local koala population from the beginning of white settlement. He found that koalas were not mentioned in any account prior to 1850, occasionally sighted in the early 1850s, abundant by the late 1860s and present in thousands in some areas between 1870 and 1890. Parris observed that this increase coincided with the annihilation of the resident Aboriginal tribe and suggested that it was their hunting that had previously kept koala numbers low.

EUROPEAN EXPLOITATION

By the second half of the nineteenth century it appears that koalas were sufficiently abundant for Europeans to take up hunting them. HW Wheelwright, the 'old bushman', was part of the great influx of Europeans that arrived in Victoria during the gold rush years of the early 1850s. He had trained as a lawyer but apparently could not make a living out of either law or gold in the colonies, and ended up supplying the Melbourne market with game animals that he shot on the nearby Mornington Peninsula. He observed that koala flesh was edible — 'not unlike that of the northern bear in taste' — and that it was 'considered a delicacy by the blacks'. He also noted that koalas were 'extremely difficult to shoot on account of their thick hide'.

The toughness of koalas — so tough that bullets would bounce off them — was legend. Dudley le Souef, director of Melbourne's Zoological Gardens in the 1890's, considered them more tenacious of life 'than the proverbial cat'. He illustrated this with an account of an incident he observed when he accompanied a party of tree-fellers into the Gembrook forest, east of Melbourne:

> I saw on one occasion a large forest tree over two hundred feet [60 metres] high cut down. It fell with a thunderous crash, making the ground tremble, and when looking at the wreck, I noticed a Bear lying on the ground that had come down with the tree. We all looked at the animal, thinking of course that it was dead, but when the men had gone on with their chopping I saw it slowly open it eyes and look round, and seeing no one moving near it, it

commenced slowly crawling to the nearest tree; but one of the men caught sight of it, and before he could be stopped, had knocked it on the head with the back of an axe and apparently finished it. Shortly afterwards, however, I again saw it open its eyes and quietly look around; and, seeing the coast clear, it again made for a neighbouring tree and this time was successful, as it surely deserved to be.

THE FUR TRADE

By the late nineteenth century European settlement was spreading rapidly. A skin and fur trade sprang up, largely driven by white setters selling pelts to supplement their meagre income from farming. Koala, kangaroo, wallaby and possum skins were all taken, and local dealers sold them into the European and later the American fur market. In areas where koalas were abundant, it was obviously easy (and relatively lucrative) to shoot large numbers of these sedentary, tree-dwelling and diurnally visible animals. Lydekker, the author of an early text on marsupials, commented:

> ... the koala must be an abundant animal, since from 10,000 to 30,000 skins are annually imported into London, while in 1889 the enormous total of 300,000 was reached .... they are mainly used in the manufacture of those articles for which a cheap and durable fur is required.

Market reports from 1906 show the comparative value of koala pelts which were worth up to 19.5 pence each, while those of possums were up to 18 pence and the best quality large grey kangaroo skins were up to 90 pence each.

By the early 1900s the fur trade had declined in the southern states but continued in Queensland. One million koala skins were sold in the open season of 1919 and as many as two million were estimated to have been exported in 1924 (many of them deliberately mislabled as 'wombat'). This slaughter revolted the general public and the controversy surrounding the last open season on koalas in Queensland (August, 1927) is well documented. Even the Archbishop of Brisbane entered the debate, calling for state-wide protests. He stated that: 'If the Acting Premier realises how very deep an offence the permission to destroy native bears has given a vast number of quiet, peaceable, decent-minded people, the permission would be withdrawn'. Amen, your Grace. The Acting Premier eventually did act, but only after 584,738 koala skins had been traded at an average price of 56 shillings and 9 pence per dozen.

This over-harvesting is one of the reasons advanced to explain the apparent decline of the koala that took place in many parts of its range in the early decades of the twentieth century. It is suggested that by the early 1900s it had been shot to extinction in the remnant forests in the south-east of South Australia. The decline prompted wide-spread public concern about its fate and the koala soon became a protected species throughout its range: first in Victoria in 1898, then in New South Wales in 1903, followed by Queensland in 1906 and South Australia in 1912

A PROTECTED SPECIES

With protection, koala populations recovered to their former abundance in some areas. The Wilson's Promontory population, in southern Victoria, did so but with unanticipated consequences.

Wilson's Promontory, Victoria's first National Park, was permanently reserved as a wildlife sanctuary in 1908. Heavily timbered and free of settlers, it was a pristine place to set aside for the preservation of native fauna. Prior to 1898, the year the koala became a protected species in Victoria, shooting parties were in the habit of visiting the Promontory to obtain koala skins each winter. One account reporting these shooters taking up to 2000 pelts a year. Once pelt-shooting stopped, koala numbers began to increase and within a few years they had become so numerous that they were defoliating and killing their preferred food species, the swamp gum (*Eucalyptus ovata*), in many areas. The response of the park's management was to reduce the number of koalas in these areas. Where possible animals were captured and translocated to other parts of the park but in inaccessible areas and in the taller timber, a number of koalas were shot. This relieved the browsing pressure on the trees for a short time but, once they sprouted new leaves, koalas moved in from surrounding areas and stripped this new growth until they eventually killed the trees. The Field Naturalists Club of Victoria visited one such site in the Darby River area in 1915 and observed that: 'what was once a thickly-timbered eucalyptus forest, where, only a few years ago native bears [might be seen] is now a mass of dead and bleached trees'. With their favoured food species virtually eliminated, these coastal populations disappeared. The koala survived on Wilson's Promontory, but largely in the blue gum (*E. globulus*) clad ranges of the interior. They have not since attained the abundance that they once enjoyed in the coastal swamp gum forests.

The history of the population in the Bega Valley in New South Wales suggests that another factor, more potent than harvesting, was responsible for the abrupt decline in koalas there. Pelt shooters had also been very active in the Bega district, particularly in 1870s and 1880s, but no reduction in the koala population was noted before 1905. Between 1905 and 1910, however, the koala population declined alarmingly, reportedly with hundreds of animals found dead at the base of trees. At the time there were no reports of over-browsing or defoliation of food trees, and it was commonly believed that the animals were stricken with a disease. Koalas have remained rare in the Bega area right up to the present day.

DISEASE

Infectious disease has been suggested to be the major cause of the abrupt decline in koala numbers which took place in many places in the late nineteenth and during the early years of the twentieth century. Epidemics of disease and associated population collapse were reported from many localities from across the range of the koala. Ellis Troughton, at the time the Curator of Mammals at the Australian Museum in Sydney, referred to some form of ophthalmic (eye) disease that was said to have 'swept away millions of koalas in the years 1887–9 and 1900–3'. Unfortunately neither Troughton nor anyone else left a comprehensive description of the pathology, or diagnosis of the cause, of this disease.

Over recent years a suite of disease conditions in the koala have been attributed to infection with the bacterium *Chlamydia*. Some of these are of an 'ophthalmic' nature with chlamydiosis of the eye, usually known as 'pink-eye' or keratoconjunctivis, a common condition. *Chlamydia* also causes pathological changes in the urino-genital tract and JP Hill, an anatomist from the University of Sydney, observed a condition that he referred to as 'cystic ovaries' in many of the koalas that he collected from northern New South Wales and south-east Queensland in the 1890s. In many ways the 'ophthalmic disease' which is thought to have razed koala populations in the late nineteenth and early twentieth centuries resembles 'pink-eye' and this, together with Hill's observations, suggests that *Chlamydia* may well have been the pathogen involved. The impact of *Chlamydia* on koala populations, particularly its effect on fertility and consequently on abundance, is still a perplexing issue today and we will deal with it in greater detail in Chapters 6 and 7.

CLEARING OF NATIVE FOREST

In the gold rush years, starting in 1851, a large number of people emigrated to southern Australia and the pace of settlement increased markedly. Large areas of land were cleared to support this rapidly increasing population. The most fertile and accessible land, often along the river flats, was usually cleared first as it had the greatest agricultural potential. These areas also supported the most productive eucalypt forests and, from our present knowledge of the dietary and habitat preferences of koalas, would have contained the most abundant populations. Consequently this clearing probably eliminated the best koala habitat and, combined with the impacts of pelt shooting and disease, brought about the demise of koala populations in many districts.

Clearing of native forest has continued unabated to the present day. It is estimated that an average of 360,000 hectares of forest have been cleared for each of the 200 years of European settlement in Australia. At the present time the dry country in central Queensland, marginal agricultural land that contains low abundance koala populations, is being cleared at a rate in excess of 500,000 hectares per year. Such clearing remains a major issue for koala conservation today, particularly for the northern populations, but we will discuss this further in Chapter 8.

BUSHFIRE

By the 1920s and 1930s many prominent naturalists were pessimistic about the koala's future. Reviewing the situation in Victoria at this time, the Chief Inspector of Wildlife, Fred Lewis, estimated that there were probably less than 1000 koalas surviving in the whole of the state. While recognising the role of land-clearing, pelt shooting and disease in their decline, he saw the most significant factor to be the large-scale bushfires that had plagued Victoria since the earliest days of white settlement.

Koalas, being arboreal and relatively slow-moving animals, have no way of escaping forest fires and are wiped out by them, often over considerable areas. However, the eucalypt forests of south-eastern Australia are one of the most fire-prone habitats on earth, and probably have been since the early Pleistocene. This raises the question as to how koalas have survived fire in these forests for so long. Presuming Fred Lewis was right, and fire was the key, why had it taken until the early years of the twentieth century for it to become such a threat to them? Unfortunately, we do not have a precise answer to this question. It is suspected that it had something to do with changes in the nature of forest fires, especially their intensity and frequency, after the arrival of the Europeans.

Prior to the arrival of Europeans, the Aboriginal people burnt the country relentlessly. The practice was so widespread that it caused Captain James Cook, on his first voyage of exploration up the eastern coastline in 1770, to refer to Australia as 'This continent of smoke'. The indigenous people had a number of reasons for doing this, including warfare (many of the early white explorers had a fire sent downwind onto their camp by hostile Aborigines) but they primarily used it for what has come to be known as 'firestick farming'. That is, early spring fires being lit to encourage certain food plants, as well as provide green pick to attract kangaroos and wallabies into open areas to facilitate hunting.

A consequence of this fire regime was the maintenance of grasses as a prominent feature of the forest floor, with little build-up of litter or regrowth of woody shrubs. Many accounts by early settlers described the park-like appearance of the original forests: giant old eucalyptus trees with the ground so free of undergrowth that you could gallop a horse through them. Modern experience with fuel reduction burning suggests that these traditional burning practices would have also reduced the frequency and intensity of crown fires. We have no information on their impact on koalas but, given the huge size of the trees and the fact that these fires would have been largely confined to the forest floor, it is likely to have been slight.

The early European settlers had no concept of how the Australian landscape had long been manicured by fire and initially did not follow the fire practices of the Aborigines. As a consequence fuel accumulated on the forest floor and the fires that then did occur were on a huge scale. The first of these conflagrations in Victoria occurred in 1851. There is virtually no information on its scale but a painting hanging in the National Gallery in Canberra gives some idea of its ferocity. Painted by the colonial artist William Strutt and entitled 'Black Thursday 1851', it shows an eerie nightscape of colonial Melbourne, backlit by the glow of a huge forest fire. In 1898 another such fire burnt almost all of Gippsland. More recently, the 1939 fire burnt more than two million hectares of forest.

Koalas are highly vulnerable to fires that burn the forest canopy, and when such fires occur koalas are eliminated over considerable areas. There is little wonder that such bushfires were seen as the major reason for the many local extinctions and the generally low number of koalas thought to be surviving in Victoria in the early 1900s. Fortuitously koalas were still abundant on some offshore islands where they had been introduced in the late 1800s. From the early 1920s onwards, surplus animals from these islands were relocated to the mainland and released back into the forests they once occupied. This aspect of koala history will be dealt with at greater length in the chapter on conservation and management (Chapter 8).

THE FUTURE

Essentially this history suggests that the koala has had a topsy turvy ride and that its populations have fluctuated markedly over time. This has certainly been the case since Europeans first came to Australia over two hundred years ago and may even have been so before then. Why this has occurred and whether it is to continue are questions that can only be addressed when we have a more complete understanding of the biology of the koala. It will take much of the remaining chapters to develop this, starting with a discussion of the koala's present day distribution and abundance.

DISTRIBUTION AND ABUNDANCE

The 'distribution' of a species is the geographical area over which it is normally found. Accurate data on this is very important information in the biological profile of any species and there is much scientific literature discussing the key factors which influence it. The consensus is that the edge of a distribution is usually determined by a combination of historical and ecological factors, the latter including climate, soil fertility and food supply.

Distribution is a major indicator of conservation status: if the distribution of a species is contracting over time, this is primary evidence that its conservation status is deteriorating. The absolute size of the area over which a species occurs is also significant. These days wild animals are subject to many nefarious influences and populations distributed over small areas are inherently more vulnerable than widely distributed ones. A single catastrophic event, such as a bushfire or an abnormally severe drought, can exterminate a small population and cause the local extinction of a species.

The distribution of a species is usually presented as an area on a map and these maps are sometimes criticised for not telling the full story on an animal's current conservation status. It is often suggested that a seemingly healthy distribution, represented by a large number of dots on a map, does not necessarily mean that the species itself is doing

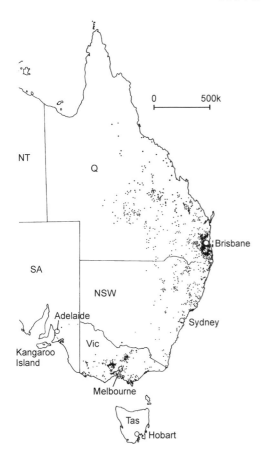

Figure 3.1
The distribution of the koala as revealed by the 1986/87 National Koala Survey. Each dot represents a locality where koalas have been recorded. (Adapted from Phillips 1990.)

well. To some extent this is true and such maps do have shortcomings. For example, they do not give any information on how 'abundant' a species is. This is important because abundance is seldom uniform between sites or static over time at a single site.

In recent years there has been a great deal of controversy over the conservation status of the koala. This culminated in 1996 when several groups petitioned the Australian Federal Government to add the koala to the list of endangered species. Many of the key arguments put by the petitioners dealt with questions of distribution and abundance.

CURRENT DISTRIBUTION OF THE KOALA

The distribution of the koala is not continuous but disjunct: that is, broken up into a number of separate populations that are isolated from each other by areas of unsuitable habitat or cleared land. Over the years many state and regional surveys have been conducted of these various populations. The first nation-wide survey was conducted by the Australian Government's National Parks and Wildlife Service in 1986 and the distribution map shown in Figure 3.1 is based on the results of that survey.

This map gives the best picture of the current distribution of the koala. The disjunct nature of this distribution largely reflects the fragmented nature of Australia's remnant forests. This fact aside, the koala is still extremely widespread with populations occurring all the way down the eastern side of the continent, from the tropical north to the temperate south. Overall, their total range stretches over some 22° of latitude and 18° of longitude and encompasses an area of around one million square kilometres. Over the 210 years since the arrival of Europeans this range has contracted somewhat but it is still a relatively broad one compared to those of most other Australian mammals. For example, the koalas nearest marsupial relative, the common wombat (*Vombatus ursinus*), is found over an area of less than 200,000 square kilometres, while Bennett's tree-kangaroo (*Dendrolagus bennettianus*), one of our rarer mammals, has a total range of less than 3000 square kilometres.

Detailed information on local distribution is also important, particularly as the management of native wildlife is the responsibility of state and territory governments. Wildlife agencies in most Australian states maintain databases for all native fauna that occurs within their borders, including locality records. This information is constantly updated and, while it is mainly obtained from faunal surveys conducted by professional biologists, amateurs with a particular interest in wildlife also make a substantial contribution. The koala is a relatively large species that does not use a den or hollow, is visible during the day and does not require either special equipment (such as traps or detectors) or special skills to detect. Because it is also a very charismatic species, koala sightings by interested members of the general public are regularly reported and added to these databases. As a result the koala data set is current and probably more complete than it is for many other Australian mammals. Figure 3.2 shows the current distribution of the koala in Victoria based on information from the database of the Atlas of Victorian Wildlife.

Figure 3.2 illustrates the point that not all distribution maps present their information in the same way. The usual method, used in Figure 3.1, is to record every locality where the species has been sighted as a dot or

Figure 3.2
Past and current distribution of the koala in Victoria (symbols), and the present remnant forest cover (shading). (Reprinted with permission from *Mammals of Victoria*, Oxford University Press and DCNR Victoria.)

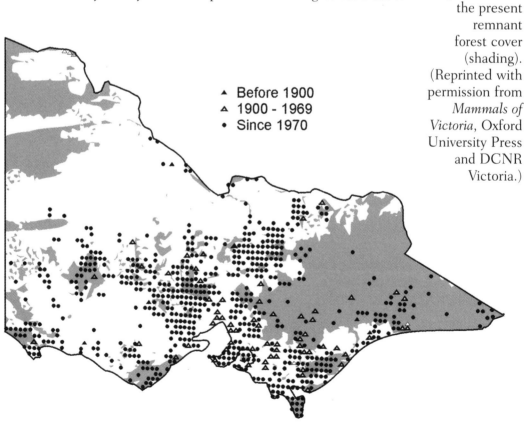

▲ Before 1900
△ 1900 - 1969
• Since 1970

a cross on the map. However, as Victoria is a relatively small place (compared to most other Australian states) and as koalas are in high abundance in many places there, the scale required of a publishable distribution map would not permit this sort of representation. In many areas all the dots would fuse together into a large blob.

To overcome this the geographical area of Victoria has been divided into 5 minute cells of latitude and longitude (rectangles of approximately 7.5 by 9.3 kilometres). A symbol in a cell indicates that koalas (at least one) have been recorded from the area. Different symbols are used for different time periods, allowing information on the age of the records to be included in the distribution map. This means that any significant distributional changes over time can be tracked (the significance of which is discussed in the following section). The main shortcoming of this type of presentation is that it does not indicate whether koalas are commonplace or rare in an area. (However more detailed information on the number of animals sighted in the area is available in the data base.)

In Figure 3.2 the locality information for koalas in Victoria is superimposed over current forest cover (as derived from GIS satellite imagery). This provides information on the extent of the forest relative to the distribution of the koala, and clearly illustrates the fact that much of Victoria's remaining forest occurs in small patches and that, in southern and central regions at least, koalas are present in most of these forest patches. They are absent from the large area of forest in the north-west of the state as this is mainly semi-arid and unsuitable habitat for koalas. They are also poorly represented in the large block of forest in the north-east and this is also unsuitable habitat for them as much of it is alpine and snow-covered for several months each winter.

CHANGES IN KOALA DISTRIBUTION

There is no precise information on the distribution of the koala at the time that Europeans first occupied Australia. From the accounts of the early explorers we believe that koalas were widespread in the forests and woodlands of eastern Australian although they appear not to have been particularly abundant (see Chapter 2). We know that tens of millions of hectares of this habitat has been cleared since the coming of the Europeans and this has undoubtedly had a major impact on the distribution and abundance of koalas (see Figure 3.3).

This loss of habitat has been accompanied by a shrinkage of the koala's range. As late as the 1940s koalas were still occasionally seen as far north as Cooktown in the far north of Queensland. Present records indicate that the most northerly populations now known occur several hundred kilometres further south, on the southern edge of the Atherton

1800　　　　　　　　1985-90

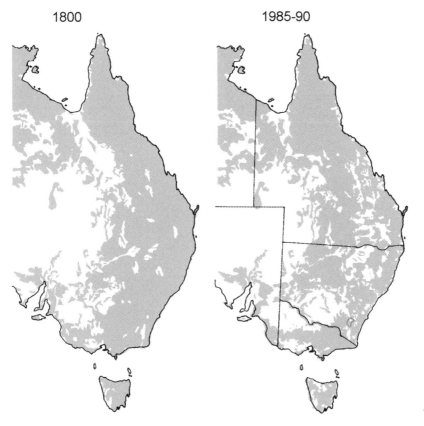

Figure 3.3
Changes in
forest cover in
Australia since
European settle-
ment in 1788.
The discrepancy
between this
representation of
Victoria's current
forests and that
of Figure 3.2 is
due to differing
definitions of
'forest cover'.
(Adapted from
*Atlas of Australian
Resources: Vege-
tation*, 3rd Series,
Volume 6,
AGPS, Canberra.)

Tablelands. The forests of south-eastern South Australia are usually considered to be the western extremity of the koalas historic range, however the explorer Edward John Eyre believed they extended even further along the southern coastline into Western Australia. During his overland journey of 1841 Eyre encountered a party of Aborigines at the head of the Great Australian Bight. One of the men was wearing a belt made from koala fur and he told Eyre that he obtained it further to the west where the animals lived in the patches of larger trees.

The once-endemic koala population in South Australia appears to have become extinct in the early decades of the twentieth century. In Victoria, koalas also declined to such low numbers in the 1920s that their extinction was considered inevitable. This situation was redeemed as a result of an extensive translocation program, and populations in some areas of South Australia have also been re-established with animals translocated from Victoria (see Chapter 8). Koalas have also become rarer in New South Wales, particularly in the south, compared with the situation there in the early years of the twentieth century.

More recent changes in the distribution of the northern koala populations have been revealed in a series of surveys conducted since 1967. The first two of these surveys, in 1967 and 1977, were conducted by the Wildlife Preservation Society of Queensland, and the most recent one, in 1986/87, was carried out by the Australian National Parks and Wildlife Service as part of their National Koala Survey. When the results of the 1967 and 1977 surveys were compared it was concluded that there had been no major expansion or contraction of the range of the koala in Queensland over that decade. However, in the 1986/87 survey, there were noticeably fewer koala locations in the far west of Queensland. This was attributed to two major causes: land clearing and a prolonged drought in the early 1980s.

Droughts have undoubtedly been a major influence on the distribution of the koala for a very long time, particularly on the populations abutting the arid zone. This western edge of the koala's distribution has probably moved back and forth over time, with populations expanding in a sequence of good seasons and contracting with drought. Greg Gordon, a wildlife scientist with the Queensland National Parks and Wildlife Service, has conducted long-term research on koalas and he documented a population crash that occurred in south-western Queensland in the drought of 1979/80. In one area more than 63 per cent of the animals died from the combined effects of malnutrition (largely because most of their food trees shed their foliage during the drought) and dehydration. Koalas that lived in better quality habitat, especially around permanent waterholes, survived. Research by Sarah Munks and her colleagues showed that in semi-arid areas of north Queensland, woodlands along drainage lines are the most important habitat for koalas. Clearly habitat associated with water courses is crucial for the survival of koala populations in drier country.

Koala populations can recover from drought and recolonise an area. They cannot recover if the forest is cleared, and clearing of native forest has continued unabated from the earliest days of European colonisation. Clearing rates in the south have slowed over recent years and this to some extent reflects an emerging conservation consciousness. However, it is also because very little of the original southern forests remain intact — after all, it was there that the Europeans settled first! The current situation in Queensland is alarming. More than 500,000 hectares of forest is still being cleared each year, most of it for agricultural pursuits of dubious economic benefit. Substantial areas of koala habitat are also being lost in coastal areas of south-east Queensland, as well as in northern New South Wales. This is mostly for residential developments to accommodate a booming population.

ABUNDANCE

The distribution map (Figure 3.1 page 29) suggests that the koala currently occupies a broad range but, as previously mentioned, distribution maps do not tell the full story. They do not contain any information on abundance. (They would be doubly useful if they did!) Therefore when looking at maps of koala distribution, it is important to bear in mind that koalas are not uniformly abundant across their range. In fact, they are found in relatively low abundance over much of it and, as a rule, are far more abundant in the forests and woodlands of the south than in the north.

Population density provides a measure of abundance, and is usually expressed as the number of animals per unit area. The range of densities encountered in natural populations from across the range of the koala are well illustrated with data from some recently published studies.

One group of the studies was conducted in the cool temperate south. One of these, by Sharon Downes and her colleagues from the University of Melbourne, studied koalas in fertile, high-rainfall country on the Strathbogie Plateau in north-eastern Victoria. They reported koala abundances in excess of eight animals per hectare from 18 sites in this area. With larger animals, such as mammals, abundances are often expressed 'per square kilometre' and Sharon's figure converts to density of over 800 koalas per square kilometre. Over the course of Peter Mitchell's three-year study of a koala population on French Island, abundance ranged between 6 and 9 animals per hectare (600–900 animals per square kilometre). In the drier Brisbane Ranges of central-west Victoria, Mark Hindell reported a koala density that fluctuated between 0.7 and 1.6 animals per hectare (70–160 animals per square kilometre). Much lower abundances than this are encountered in the remnant koala populations of the south-eastern forests of New South Wales, while in the north in the Lismore region, Bruce Gall reported abundances of around one animal per hectare (100 animals per square kilometre).

Further north still, in the tall open eucalypt forests of Redland Shire in south-eastern Queensland, Neil White and Noelene Kunst from the Queensland University of Technology, reported that koala abundance did not significantly vary from 0.4 koalas per hectare (40 koalas per square kilometre) over the 12 month period of their study.

The lower end of the abundance spectrum is well illustrated with data collected by Alistair Melzer and David Lamb from the University of Queensland. They estimated koala abundances in the Brigalow Scrubs (*Acacia harpophylla*) and associated eucalypt woodlands of the semi-arid zone of central Queensland. They did so with the help of a

Figure 3.4
Composite map showing
both the distribution
and abundance of koalas
across Australia. Each
dot marks a locality
where koalas have been
sighted and the shaded
area indicates the overall
range of the koala.
The gradient in the
shading gives a crude
indication of the level
of abundance, with
the darker shading
indicating the higher
abundance populations.
(Distribution data from
National Koala Survey
1986/87; abundance
data from the published
sources mentioned.)

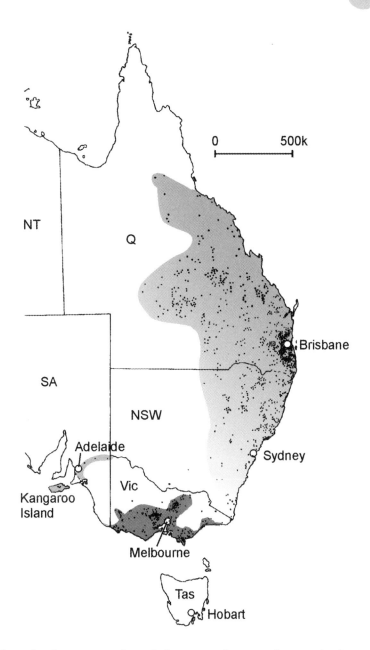

large number of volunteers and used the somewhat macabre method
of following the bulldozers that were clearing the country and count-
ing the koalas they found in the debris. They did this over 2500
hectares and found koala abundance ranged from a high of one animal per 67 hectares down to an abysmally low one animal per 210
hectares. The latter figure is slightly less than 0.5 koalas per square

kilometre. Their sample contained animals of all age classes, including breeding females, and this prompted the authors to point out that these animals were not just eking out an existence in 'poor quality habitat' but were representative of a viable and well adapted population, albeit an extremely low density one.

Figure 3.4 (page 35) attempts to illustrate the discussion of preceding paragraphs in a single diagram. The shaded area represents the current distribution of the koala and the gradient in the shading gives a crude indication of the level of abundance.

WHY DOES ABUNDANCE VARY?

The natural range of koalas encompasses forests and woodlands from arid, temperate, sub-tropical and tropical areas. Most of these areas are dominated by trees from a single genus, *Eucalyptus*, and the dietary dependence of koalas on eucalypt foliage is one of the more fascinating aspects of their biology. This is discussed at length in Chapter 4, but suffice it to say here that the various eucalypt species are not equally palatable to koalas and the abundance of koalas in a particular area is linked to the availability of the more palatable food. The growth form, species composition and productivity of eucalypt forests vary markedly across the koala's range, with productivity largely determined by soil fertility, temperature range and rainfall. These latter parameters could be regarded as the prime determinants of the 'koala carrying capacity' of a forest.

Carrying capacity is a concept more familiar to pastoralists dealing with domesticated animals. It is usually expressed as the average number of beasts supported per hectare of pasture per year. We are not used to applying this concept to wildlife species, particularly to those that live in trees, but from the examples of koala abundances we provided earlier the carrying capacity of the habitat they occupy obviously varies widely. If we wished to use this to estimate the total number of wild koalas in Australia, we would need detailed information on the area and carrying capacity of all of the forest types occupied by koalas from across the range of the species.

SO HOW MANY KOALAS ARE THERE?

Estimating the total number of individuals in any widely distributed wildlife species is a Herculean task. It is time consuming, expensive and, because of the problematic nature of estimating numbers for cryptic species, it is of dubious validity anyway. ('Cryptic' animals are those that, because of their colouration and/or behaviour, are difficult to see.) An attempt at a total count is done largely for two reasons. Firstly, it is done to satisfy the curiosity of a general public that is becoming increasingly interested in conservation. The koala is perceived by many to be an endangered species and first question often asked is 'How many are there left?'

The second reason is that total population size is now one of the criteria used by international agencies (such as the International Union for the Conservation of Nature) to rank species according to their conservation status. It is part of a set of basic facts that is used to decide whether a species is secure or should be listed as either 'vulnerable', 'endangered' or 'critically endangered'. For example, a species with a declining population of less than 10,000 individuals living in the wild would be regarded as vulnerable. Such rankings are used to assign conservation priorities and, inevitably, to allocate scarce conservation funds.

Estimates of total population size can not simply be made by looking at distribution maps and making a few calculations. Apart from the fact that they usually do not contain any information on abundance, distribution maps often represent distributions in different ways. As indicated earlier, some indicate the presence or absence of animals per 5 minute cell (such as Figure 3.2). With such maps it should be remembered that each cell represents a geographical area of around 70 square kilometres and, depending on the carrying capacity of the area, a blacked out cell could indicate anywhere between 50 and 50,000 individuals.

For the koala, a widely distributed and relatively cryptic species that often occurs in low abundance over very large areas, the question 'How many are there?' is not easy to answer. The few estimates that are around are 'guestimates' only, and should be treated with scepticism.

A LEAF EATING MARSUPIAL

An understanding of feeding ecology is extremely important for wildlife conservation. What an animal eats has a major influence on where it lives, and preserving its preferred habitat is critical if a species is to survive in the wild. The basic fact of koala feeding ecology is that they eat gum leaves. This is so widely known that it is almost part of the folklore. Gums, eucalypts, are extremely abundant and widespread on the Australian continent, and unlike many other forms of vegetation (which experience marked seasonal fluctuations in biomass) their foliage provides a high standing crop of food throughout the whole year. The ability of the koala to exploit this resource is undoubtedly one of the reasons why it occurs across such a large geographic area in comparison to many other native mammals. Koalas are, in fact, one of a very small group of marsupials that can exist entirely on a diet of eucalypt foliage. But there are hundreds of species of eucalypts, growing in a wide range of habitats, only a few of which are important to koalas.

DIET AND FEEDING BEHAVIOUR

While most people are aware of the unusual diet of koalas, surprising few have actually seen them feeding. Koalas are mostly seen in zoos and the main thing people notice about them there is their sleepiness. It is usually assumed that they are sleeping off the intoxicating effects of eating gum leaves, but this is not the case. Scientists, however, do believe that the diet and activity levels of koalas are linked but this is a complex subject.

The behaviour of captive animals is often abnormal, with listlessness and excessive sleeping a common response to captivity. However, several studies have now been completed on wild koalas and it is a consistent finding of this research that, even when living free, koalas are not particularly active. They usually feed and move around for about four hours a day. The rest of the time they sleep.

Our field studies show that while some individual koalas will feed at any time of the day or night, most feeding occurs during the first half of the night, usually between 1700 and 2400 hours. Animals do not feed continuously through this period but tend to feed in a series of six to ten bouts lasting, on average, for 20 minutes but ranging between 5 and 80 minutes in length. Weather has some influence on the timing of feeding activity, particularly in the south where it is often wet and cold during winter. Koalas usually do not feed during heavy rain: instead they remain curled up in a tight ball, which undoubtedly helps insulate them against the cold and conserve energy. During prolonged cold, wet periods they can spend a considerable amount of their time in this state. They take full advantage of any dry interludes however, and, when it stops raining, they wake up hungry. This is why a lot of koala feeding activity may be seen on a warm, dry day following a period of cold, wet weather.

Koalas often sleep in the tree in which they have been feeding. They may move to another tree between feeding bouts, but our studies on Victorian koalas show that, on average, they only do this about once every 24 hours. We have found that animals under continuous observation feed in every eucalypt they occupy. Several research groups have reported similar observations, and the trees in which koalas are observed resting during the day are often relied upon as a convenient indicator of the preferred food trees of a population. Some recent work, however, suggests that this may not always be the case. U Nyo Tun from the Department of Zoology at the University of Queensland followed a group of koalas and recorded the trees they used each day. Tun also collected faecal pellets from these animals and, by analysing the fragments of leaf in them, determined what tree species they had been feeding on. Tun found that the species preference according to the faecal analysis did not correspond with the ranking obtained from diurnal tree use, and suggested that the pattern of tree use may be more complex than other studies have suggested. Tun's results need to be borne in mind when assessing food tree preference of a population, and it is quite possible that tree use is influenced by variations in koala behaviour in different parts of

Australia. In the north, where temperatures are much higher, koalas may regularly use shade trees for resting in during the day and only move into preferred food trees during the cool of night.

This habit of koalas, of sitting in non-eucalypts, has lead people to speculate on whether they also feed on these species. Several studies have shown that they often do take foliage from non-eucalypts. In one study we introduced a small group of koalas to Chinaman Island in Western Port, Victoria, and monitored them weekly. After a few months it became apparent that they were spending an inordinate amount of time in the coast tea-tree (*Leptospermum laevigatum*) and swamp paperbark (*Melaleuca ericifolia*) that proliferated on the island. A subsequent analysis of their faecal pellets showed that while the bulk of the diet of most animals was coastal manna gum (*Eucalyptus prioriana*), they were taking a surprising amount of foliage from the tea-tree and some paperbark. Similarly, we have observed French Island koalas feeding on pine needles from the introduced Monterey Pine (*Pinus radiata*). Koalas on Magnetic Island, off Townsville in north Queensland, have been reported to feed on a number of genera other than *Eucalyptus*, including box (*Tristania*) and kapok (*Bombax*). In all of these cases, however, eucalypt leaf appears to comprise the bulk of the koalas' diet.

In Victoria, at least, the incidence of koalas feeding in non-eucalypts is usually not as high as their occupancy of these trees would suggest. As we have already intimated for the northern populations, this use of non-eucalypts most often appears to be related to the weather. On very hot or very cold days Victorian animals spend more time in species with dense foliage (such as *Banksia*, *Acacia* and *Melaleuca*), undoubtedly because these provide more shelter that the open canopy of the eucalypts. When monitored closely, many of these animals are found to move into a nearby eucalypt during the evening to feed.

The amount of leaf that a koala eats varies with body size, with larger animals eating more than smaller ones. A 10 kilogram Victorian koala, for example, will eat about 600–800 grams of leaf per day. Naturally this varies a little with the time of year and with prevailing climatic conditions. It also varies with the reproductive condition of the animal, as research by Andrew Krockenberger of the University of Sydney demonstrated. He found that free-living female koalas in a northern New South Wales population increased their food intake by about 20–25 per cent in late lactation and that this was related to the milk requirements of the large and rapidly growing young.

FUSSY FEEDERS OR LIMITED CHOICES?

Another aspect of koala feeding behaviour that it is part of folklore is that they are extremely fussy, and this is true to a degree. Field workers have noted that koalas may change their food preferences with the season, and anybody who has cared for koalas in captivity will testify that they are not the easiest of animals to feed. Sometimes they exhibit sudden shifts in feeding preference and refuse to eat foliage from a tree species that they had consumed with gusto for weeks previously. This was first noted in the 1930s by the renowned naturalist David Fleay during his days at Melbourne Zoo. Fleay observed that his captive koalas preferred to eat coastal manna gum (*E. prioriana*) for most of the year except for a period in mid-winter when they would not touch it.

David Fleay could not explain his koalas' fastidiousness, but Ambrose Pratt attributed it to the presence of prussic acid (cyanide) in the leaves of manna gums at this time of year. This has since been investigated by several workers but never confirmed. Some years ago Eric Conn, an American researcher interested in cyanogenic activity in plants, conducted a wide scale survey of eucalypts in south-eastern Australia and while prussic acid was present in some species, he found it to be extremely rare in manna gums. A more recent study, by Rob Bednarik from the University of Melbourne, found no evidence of cyanogenic activity in the species browsed by koalas on Phillip Island.

Myths and misconceptions about what koalas actually eat and why they do so still abound. Contrary to popular belief, they do not feed on gum tips (juvenile foliage) alone. While koalas may feed eagerly on the tips of some eucalypt species, Ben Moore, from the Australian National University, recently showed that they actually avoid the tips of otherwise preferred species, such as *E. globulus*. In reality, the bulk of the diet consists of relatively mature foliage. Wild koalas simply do not have year round access to enough young leaf tips to meet their nutritional requirements. Juvenile foliage is only abundant in spring and summer and even then it is largely restricted to the ends of small branches. While accessible to juvenile animals, these small branches are not always strong enough to support the weight of the larger adults.

The most common misconception about koalas is that they will eat only one or two of the 600 or so eucalypt species that occur in Australia. While it is true that koalas in a local area will usually concentrate on a small number of eucalypt species from the range available, over their geographic range they feed on many different species. The suite of species that they feed on at one site may be quite different to what they feed on at another (see Table 4.1). Food preference can also vary over a relatively small geographic area. In coastal areas of south eastern Victoria, for example, *E. radiata* is rarely eaten by koalas, while a few hundred kilometres inland, in the Strathbogie Ranges in north central Victoria, it is one of their staple food species.

Table 4.1

Eucalypt food species and other genera of trees utilised by koalas across their geographic range on a state by state basis. Species listed in the first column are highly preferred. Preference for those in the centre column may vary between localities. (Note: this list is not exhaustive. Other species are utilised locally within each state. For NSW, see Reed *et al.* 1991, Pahl & Hume 1991; Vic, Warneke 1978; Qld, White & Kunst 1991.)

State	Highly preferred *Eucalyptus* spp.	Less frequently eaten *Eucalyptus* spp.	Other genera of trees utilised
Queensland	*E. tereticornis* *E. camaldulensis* *E. propinqua* *E. microcorys*	*E. crebra* *E. populnea* *E. tessellaris* *E. fibrosa* *E. umbra* *E. resinifera* *E. orgadophila* *E. coolabah* *E. (= Corymbia) maculata*	*Tristania* *Angophora* *Melaleuca* *Lophostemon* *Acacia*
New South Wales	*E. tereticornis* *E. punctata* *E. saligna* *E. microcorys* *E. pilularis* *E. propinqua*	*E. racemosa* *E. viminalis* *E. camaldulensis* *E. ovata* *E. grandis* *E. acaciiformis*	*Acacia* *Allocasuarina* *Lophostemon*
Victoria	*E. viminalis* *E. prioriana* *E. ovata* *E. globulus* *E. camaldulensis*	*E. obliqua* *E. radiata* *E. goniocalyx* *E. macrorhyncha* *E. tereticornis* *E. camphora* *E. polyanthemos* *E. regnans* *E. rubida*	*Acacia* *Banksia* *Leptospermum* *Melaleuca* *Casuarina*
South Australia	*E. viminalis* *E. camaldulensis* *E. leucoxylon*		

There is also variation in food preferences between individual koalas at the same site, but this is not understood. Some anecdotal information suggests that an individual's preference may in part be related to that of its mother. In other words, young koalas are most likely to eat the tree species onto which they were weaned (a bit like children from India having a taste for very hot food).

To make matters even more confusing, koalas also show strong preferences for individual trees within a species. In many places in Victoria where koalas are very abundant it is quite common to see two eucalypts of the same species standing within metres of each other, one heavily browsed and the other untouched. What is the basis for this? To understand why koalas prefer some eucalypt species, or even individual trees within a species, over others, it is necessary to delve a little deeper into the mysteries of herbivory and the constraints it imposes on those who practise it.

THE CONSTRAINTS OF HERBIVORY

Herbivores (animals that feed on grass or leaves) have a very tight energy budget compared to carnivores. This is because they have to survive on a relatively poor diet. The leaves of plants contain low concentrations of important nutrients, such as nitrogen (contained in protein) and phosphorous, and large amounts of structural material (contained in plant cell walls), such as cellulose and lignin. While cellulose contains energy that animals can use, mammals lack the special enzymes needed to digest it. Mammalian herbivores therefore need to eat large amounts of plant material to meet their energy requirements and, because the structural components of plants impede digestion, the rate of digestion, and the rate of energy uptake, is slow.

This imposes constraints on body size and it is difficult for a small animal to survive as a herbivore because they have high energy requirements (per unit of body weight) compared with larger animals. This is largely because of their high ratio of surface area to volume, and the amount of body heat they lose to the environment as a consequence of this. From the results of a number of studies the lower limit is a body weight of around 20 kilograms. It is generally believed that animals weighing less than this will have difficulty surviving solely on a diet high in plant fibre. Koalas, which generally weigh less than 15 kilograms, fall below this line and must therefore select the best quality foliage to maximise their energy intake.

Environmental factors, such as soil fertility and moisture, slope and aspect, all influence leaf quality, and are thought to play a role in the food preferences and on habitat selection by marsupials that feed on foliage. However, in our research we have found that koala distribution and abundance is not fully explained by such factors. In fact, some of the most abundant and fecund populations of koalas occur on very nutrient-poor soils, such as those occurring along the coast and offshore islands of South Gippsland in Victoria. Recent research indicates that the food preferences of koalas are influenced far more by other aspects of leaf chemistry.

As well as being relatively low in essential nutrients, eucalypt leaves contain compounds that impede digestion or are potentially toxic to most animals. These compounds, known as 'secondary plant metabolites', are thought to be produced by plants as a defence against herbivores. They have no other apparent function. There are a number of these secondary metabolites in eucalypts, including phenolics and terpenes. (Terpenes are also known as essential oils, and it is these volatile oils that give eucalypt trees their characteristic smell.) The main consequence of ingesting these is that koalas must use some of their hard-won energy and protein to detoxify and excrete these compounds. Given that eucalypt leaves are already low in nutrients (see Table 4.2), this makes it even more amazing that koalas can survive on such a diet.

Table 4.2

Chemical composition of mature *Eucalyptus* foliage, digestibility of various *E. punctata* leaf constituents and their contribution to the energy requirements of the koala. (Data derived from Cork, Hume and Dawson 1983, Cork and Sanson 1991 and Hume 1999.)

Eucalyptus leaf constituent	% of leaf by dry weight	% of various leaf constituents digested	% contribution to energy requirements
Cell contents:			
starch and sugars	11	92	29
crude protein	10	45	29
lipids	14	43	23
total phenolics	20	91	2
Cell walls:	42		
cellulose/hemicellulose		31 / 24	17
lignin		19	0

Clearly koalas must have a range of strategies to enable them to deal with the problems of feeding on plants that are both low in digestible energy and highly toxic. One approach is to adapt behaviour so as to minimise energy expenditure. Reducing activity is the best way to do this and, as we mentioned earlier, koalas sleep a great deal.

Even when awake, they do not move rapidly unless they absolutely have to. A second behavioural strategy is to maximise their acquisition of energy by carefully selecting their food. Koalas certainly appear to do this and only feed on certain species and even then carefully smell foliage before they eat it.

Scientists believe that animals generally select the highest quality food available to them, but determining the basis of their food selection is an extremely complex task. It is thought that animals feeding on plants containing secondary metabolites make trade-offs, striking a balance to maximise nutrient intake while minimising the intake of toxic compounds. Bill Foley from the Australian National University, and Steve Cork from CSIRO Wildlife and Ecology in Canberra, have been conducting research on the feeding and digestive strategies of marsupials that feed primarily on eucalypts for many years. Recent work by Bill and his group indicates that, contrary to previous opinion, the presence of high concentrations of particular secondary plant metabolites may be the ultimate factor driving leaf selection by these animals.

While investigating diet selection in the common ringtail possum, Foley and Ivan Lawler found that the concentration of terpenes and a specific group of phenolic compounds, known as diformylphloroglucinols or DFPs (which are phenols bonded to common leaf terpenes), varied between individual *Eucalyptus ovata* and *E. viminalis* trees. There was a clear correlation between DFPs (and to a lesser degree terpenes) and food intake, with the ringtails reducing their intake of leaves containing high levels of DFPs. Over 80 per cent of variation in intake of eucalypt foliage by the possums was explained by the presence of a single compound, macrocarpal G. The researchers found no consistent correlation between food intake and the levels of nutrients, tannins or total phenolics, and concluded that DFPs were the major factor influencing foliage choice.

Foley and his team also conducted feeding trials on koalas, using *E. ovata* and *E. viminalis* foliage, and found that as the concentration of DFPs in leaves increased foliage intake decreased. However, koalas were able to feed on foliage that the possums were unable to eat, indicating that koalas can deal with higher levels of DFPs than ringtails. The researchers suggested that koalas may be better at transforming (detoxifying) and excreting DFPs than ringtails. Another member of Foley's group, Ben Moore, is currently continuing the investigation on the influence that high concentrations of DFPs have on koala leaf choice. His data, collected during feeding trials using five eucalypt species, show that individual trees within each species vary considerably in their palatability to koalas. Further, around 70 per cent of the variation in intake of foliage by koalas was due to variation in DFP concentration in leaves.

The factors that dictate the feeding preferences of koalas have long been one of the most intriguing aspects of their biology. This research by Bill Foley and his colleagues is a major breakthrough in our understanding of this issue. The fact that the concentration of these phenolic compounds varies between trees of the same species provides the first real clue as to why animals in the wild feed heavily on some individual trees of a particular species and ignore others. This information has important implications for conservation: in particular it may be very useful in assisting us with restoration of koala habitat.

THE KOALA DIGESTIVE SYSTEM

Another of the koala's strategies to deal with a poor quality and potentially toxic diet is the development of a specialised digestive system. The digestive systems of herbivores in general are much larger than those of comparably sized carnivores, and the koala has one of the most capacious digestive tracts (for its body size) of any herbivore. This assists them in dealing with their inauspicious diet.

Mammalian digestive systems are made up of a series of functional regions that perform different tasks during the process of digestion. The first part of the digestive tract, the mouth and the teeth, are designed for acquiring food and preparing it for digestion. In herbivores the teeth have two major roles. First, they must rupture the plant cells and liberate the concentrated nutrients they contain. Second, they must cut up the food into small particles to ready it for digestion further down the tract. Herbivores rely on microbial assistance to digest their food and small particle size is essential because it provides a larger surface area to volume ratio for the microbes to work on.

When feeding, koalas usually select a single leaf at a time, and the incisors at the front of the mouth are used for grasping and positioning this leaf in the mouth for further mastication. There is a gap (called the diastema) between the incisors and the most important teeth, the cheek teeth, which occur further back in the mouth. The cheek teeth are comprised of a single premolar and four molars on each of the upper and lower jaws (see Plates 2 and 3, and Fig. 2.1, page 11). The premolars are used to snip the leaf off at the petiole. The molars then take over and, as the koala chews, their high cusps pass across each other like shears. This action cuts the leaf into very small pieces and releases the cell contents (which contain starch, sugars and proteins). These appear to be one of the most important sources of energy for koalas.

In terms of nutrition, it is important for koalas to chew the leaf into small particles. This is illustrated well in old animals, in whom the cusps of the cheek teeth are worn flat (see Figure 5.9, page 70) and do not cut the leaf as finely. As a result the food in the digestive tracts of old animals contains more larger particles than in young animals. This results in inefficient digestion of these particles, and probably contributes to malnutrition and the eventual death of old koalas.

The next main functional region of the digestive tract is the stomach. In herbivores such as kangaroos and sheep the stomach is large and complex. The stomachs of these animals contain large and specialised populations of micro-organisms, including bacteria, protists and fungi. The main role of these is to break down the plant material that herbivores eat. This occurs by a process of fermentation, and because part of the stomach is modified to act as a fermentation chamber these animals are known as 'foregut fermenters'. In this type of system the major sources of nutrients for the host are the products from fermentation (such as volatile fatty acids) and protein derived from the bodies of the micro-organisms. In contrast the koala has a relatively small and simple stomach (see Figure 4.1), except for the presence of a large digestive gland. After passing through the stomach, the food enters the small intestine. Steve Cork and his colleagues have shown that more than 80 per cent of the energy a koala requires comes from the digestion of the cell contents of eucalypt leaves in the small intestine (see Table 4.2, page 44). This is surprising, as koalas also possess a large fermentation chamber.

Figure 4.1
The digestive tract of the koala.
(Modified from Schultz 1976.)

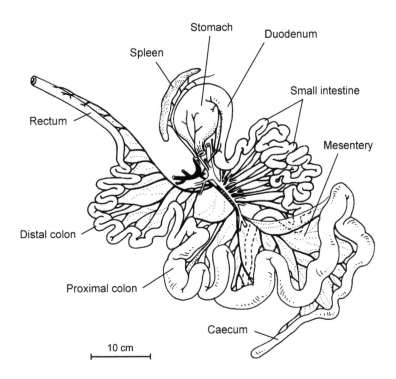

Stomach

Duodenum

Spleen

Small intestine

Rectum

Mesentery

Distal colon

Proximal colon

Caecum

10 cm

In contrast to kangaroos, koalas (and possums that feed on eucalypt foliage) have their fermentation chamber towards the hind end of the digestive tract and are called 'hindgut fermenters'. In koalas the fermentation chamber includes the caecum and proximal colon, and both are greatly enlarged to fulfil this role. (Early anatomists commented that, for its body size, the koala had an extremely large caecum.) The koala's caecum contains enormous numbers of microbes. For example in one study the average number of bacteria counted per gram of wet caecal contents was approximately 1.1×10^{10} anaerobes, plus 9.7×10^6 aerobes.

One of the more striking characteristics of digestion in koalas is the length of time food remains in the digestive tract. Long retention times are a feature of all herbivores that rely on fermentation, because of the time required by micro-organisms to break down plant material. A significant feature of koalas, however, is their ability to selectively retain part of their food for longer fermentation while allowing the rest to pass through more rapidly. Early work by Steve Cork and his colleagues showed that solutes are retained in the digestive tracts of captive koalas for up to 200 hours and this was among the longest retention times of any mammal. More recent research by Andrew Krockenberger indicates that mean retention time of solutes in wild koalas is shorter, in the order of 100 hours. It is thought that this selective retention of small particles (which have a large surface area compared to their volume) allows for their more efficient digestion by micro-organisms. In contrast, larger particles pass through more rapidly and this is thought to be advantageous to the koala because these would take more time to digest, thereby filling up the gut and reducing the efficiency of digestion.

Despite the huge degree of specialisation of the koala hindgut, its role in acquiring energy is still not fully understood. Only a small proportion of energy is derived from the process of hindgut fermentation (see Table 4.2). Its major role appears to be in the retention and recycling of nitrogen, and for an animal feeding on such a nitrogen-poor food this is obviously extremely important.

The larger leaf particles that are not retained in the caecum and proximal colon proceed on through the distal colon, where water is reabsorbed. This results in the formation of coarse textured, dry faecal pellets. This process is undoubtedly a water conservation strategy as koalas rarely drink in the wild, obtaining moisture from the leaves that they feed on.

OTHER ADAPTATIONS FOR ENERGY CONSERVATION

Metabolic rate, which is the rate at which chemical processes take place in the body, influences the amount of energy and therefore food that an animal requires. Koalas are often reported as having a lower than expected metabolic rate for a marsupial of their body size. However, this is not entirely true. Andrew Krockenberger reported the winter field metabolic rate (FMR) of 6 kilogram female koalas as 1772 kilojoules per day, which is close to the value predicted for a typical marsupial of this body weight. He further reported the FMR of female koalas to be lower than this in summer. Ken Nagy, from the University of California in Los Angeles, reported that the winter FMR of male koalas to be lower than that of females. Overall, the metabolic rate of koalas may be lower than other marsupials but there are seasonal and sex differences and these are often overlooked when broad comparisons are made between species.

NUTRITION AND HABITAT REQUIREMENTS

Living on a tight energy budget is a key theme in the biology of the koala. It enables them to survive on a poor quality diet, and requires them to be very selective about the type of eucalypt leaf they eat. This selectively has major implications for both the type and amount of habitat that koalas require for survival. The concept of 'carrying capacity' was raised in Chapter 3. This is usually quantified as the number of animals that are supported by a specified area (usually a hectare) of habitat. The converse of this — the amount of space required for an individual koala to live — is another important concept in their ecology. This space is called a 'home range' and it is defined as the area an individual animal uses during its normal activities, such as obtaining food, gaining access to mates, and raising young.

Social interactions are often an important determinant of the size of home ranges in mammals, but research conducted in Victoria by Peter Mitchell, and more recently by Rob Bednarik, suggests that this is not the case with koalas. In experimental studies of spatial use, neither the introduction of new koalas nor the removal of residents affected the home range size of the remaining residents. In contrast, the availability of highly preferred food trees does correlate with home range size: koalas living in habitat dominated by preferred food trees have relatively small home ranges, while home ranges are larger in forests containing a mixture of preferred and less palatable tree species. This suggests that the availability of sufficient palatable (preferred) food trees is a major determinant of home range size in koalas. Other factors, such as individual body weights, also have an influence. For example male koalas are substantially larger than females and several studies have shown that the home ranges of males are approximately 50 per cent larger.

So how much space does a koala need? Unfortunately it is difficult to generalise as we only have data on the sizes of home ranges
from a limited number of areas. Nevertheless these serve to illustrate
the point. In Victoria, in Peter Mitchell's study of koalas living in pure
stands of *E. viminalis*, which is one of the most highly preferred local
food tree species, the mean adult male range area was 1.7 hectares,
and the mean adult female ranges were 1.2 hectares. In a comparable
study by Mark Hindell, in a mixed forest in the Brisbane Ranges,
Victoria (Plate 4), containing six eucalypt species of variable palatability, home ranges were larger, with means of 3.1 hectares for adult
males and 2.1 hectares for females. For areas where preferred food
trees are at very low density, as in semi-arid areas of central
Queensland Alistair Melzer found home ranges to be substantially
larger again, with some males moving over areas in excess of 100
hectares.

These results emphasise the point that when thinking about koala
habitat and what constitutes good quality for koalas, it must be kept
in mind that the forests they live in are not uniform. They differ in
terms of the tree species available, the relative abundance of preferred species, and the palatability, size and quality of individual trees.
Some habitat may consist entirely of highly preferred trees, other
habitats may contain some preferred trees interspersed with non-
palatable trees. Thus the home ranges of koalas will vary in different
areas. This is one reason why the density of koalas varies across the
geographic range of the species (see Chapter 3). It should also be kept
in mind that, while the presence of high abundance populations is
good evidence that habitat quality is high, the converse is not necessarily true. Low population density may result from a range of other
factors, including variation in reproductive rates, the recent occurrence of catastrophic events such as bushfires, or the arrival of new
pathogens. Information on the home range requirements of a species
in various parts of its geographic range is a more useful indicator of
habitat quality.

BEHAVIOUR, SOCIALITY AND LIFE CYCLE

As discussed in the previous chapter, having a low energy intake places major ecological constraints on an animal. Koalas show a number of adaptations, both anatomical and behavioural, that enable them to deal with this. The brain, the organ that, above all others, controls complex behaviours, may be one of these.

'... A BEAR OF VERY LITTLE BRAIN'

So said AA Milne of Winnie the Pooh, the fictional bear with probable koala antecedents. In 1929, a year after Pooh was so abashed, Jones and Porteus's more scholarly work on the comparative anatomy of animal brains appeared. The senior author was Frederick Wood Jones, the anatomist and former Curator of Mammals at the South Australian Museum, and he was undoubtedly familiar with koalas. (He was a leading figure in the Flora and Fauna Protection Board that introduced koalas to Kangaroo Island in the 1920s, discussed in Chapter 8.) In their book Jones and Porteus describe the brain of the koala as being 'ridiculously small'. This observation lay dormant in the literature for many years until it was revived by neuro-anatomists John Haight from the University of Tasmania and John Nelson from Monash University. In a comparative study of brains from

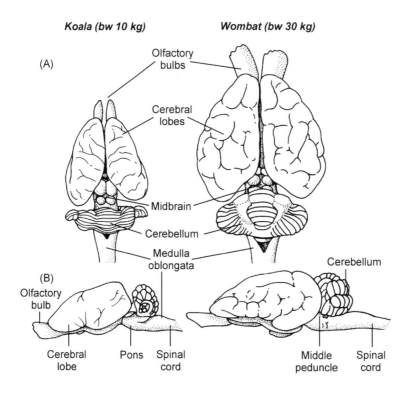

Koala (bw 10 kg)   *Wombat (bw 30 kg)*

(A)

Olfactory
bulbs

Cerebral
lobes

Midbrain

Cerebellum

Medulla
oblongata

(B)
Olfactory
bulb

Cerebellum

Cerebral   Pons   Spinal
lobe   cord

Middle   Spinal
peduncle   cord

Figure 5.1
Dorsal (A)
and lateral (B)
views of the
brains of the
koala, and its
nearest marsupi-
al relative, the
wombat. Much
of the difference
in brain size can
be attributed to
the difference
in body size.
The brain of the
koala, however, is
smaller than pre-
dicted for a mar-
supial of its body
weight and some
of its structures
are simpler than
those seen in
the wombat. The
surfaces of the
koala's cerebral
lobes, for exam-
ple, are relatively
smooth, lacking
the folding seen
in the wombat.
The cerebellum
of the koala is
also relatively
smaller than that
of the wombat
and there are
relatively larger
spaces between
the various lobes
of the koala brain.

33 marsupial species, Haight and Nelson reported that the koala brain was, in relative terms, one of the smallest they had examined. In fact it was about 60 per cent smaller than predicted for a diprotodont marsupial of an equivalent body size. They also observed that many of its structures were simplified or reduced in size when compared to other marsupials, particularly the wombat which is the koala's closest diprotodont relative (see Figure 5.1). The cerebral hemispheres of the koala's brain were, for example, small and shrunken in appearance and there was very little folding on the surface of brain. In advanced mammals with larger brains, the brain surface is folded to enable the cellular, grey matter (*neopallium*) on the surface to keep step with the huge increase in fibre volume in the inner brain. A smooth brain is characteristic of a primitive animal.

Haight and Nelson also observed that, based on the volume of the endocranial space (the brain-case), the koala brain weighed much less than expected. It was not because the brain did not fit the brain-case: they noted that both the cerebrum and cerebellum were clearly pressed up against the inner surface of the cranial vault. The lightness was because there were significant hollow regions within the koala brain itself. In the living animal these hollow areas are filled with cerebro-spinal fluid and the authors commented that the koala brain in fact resembled one experiencing the pathological condition of hydrocephaly. This caused other scientists to speculate on the function of these copious amounts of fluid within the koala's brain. (Some suggested that it may act to absorb shock and thus cushion the brain from impact when koalas fell out of trees. However, not everyone took their suggestion seriously.)

Haight and Nelson did consider the consequences of the small size and comparative impoverishment of the koala's brain (particularly in those regions dealing with fine motor control) and suggested it would render the animals slow and clumsy. However, few field workers who have handled wild koalas would agree with this. Koalas may appear lethargic because they sleep a great deal but, when roused, slow and clumsy they are not.

A more likely consequence of having such a small brain is to be found in the scope of the behavioural repertoire. Compared to most other mammals koalas show a limited range of behaviours, and a limited capacity to vary from these or to learn new ones. The stereotypical nature of their method of feeding is a good example of this. If you watch a koala feed you will find that it always goes through the same routine: it will reach forward with a forepaw and grasp a small branch, sniff the leaves and, if acceptable, begin eating them. It is widely known among zoo keepers that captive koalas are very finicky about how their food is presented to them. They will only eat leaves that are still attached to a branch with the branch supported as if it were still attached to a tree. If a koala is presented with the freshest eucalypt leaves from its most preferred species, but laid out on a dish rather than attached to a branch, it can not work out how to feed on them.

It is hard to imagine how a small brain could be of any adaptive value, but an explanation may lie in the suggestion recently made by Tim Flannery of the Australian Museum. Energy-wise, brains are very expensive organs to run and, for their size, consume a disproportionate amount of the body's total energy budget. Flannery suggested that the koala's small brain was an adaptive response to their low energy diet. A small brain would certainly help balance the energy budget and the consequence of such an adaptation would probably be a simplified and somewhat restricted behavioural repertoire. Koalas certainly have this, but it is obviously adequate for their simplified lifestyle: it has enabled the species to persist, relatively unchanged, over some 25 million years of evolutionary history.

ACTIVITY AND SOCIAL PATTERNS

Animals can also make behavioural adaptations to conserve energy, and resting a lot is an excellent strategy. Anyone who has looked at koalas, either in a wildlife park or in the wild, would know that they spend most of their time asleep, usually curled up and in the fork of a tree but always asleep. Contrary to the popular belief that koalas are constantly intoxicated by eucalypt leaves, this inactivity seems to be a method of coping with poor quality feed.

Peter Mitchell, from Monash University, spent several years studying the behaviour of koalas at Red Bill Creek on French Island, and did a detailed analysis of their activity patterns. He found that dominant males moved the most frequently, ranged over the largest area and had the highest level of social encounters. The ranges occupied by these males were stable over the three years of the study, but no single animal occupied an area exclusively and individual male's ranges overlapped extensively with those of other males and females. For example, the largest range of a male overlapped with those of ten other males and nine females, indicating that koalas are not territorial. (Territorial species defend their home range against intrusions by other individuals.)

As well as there being a great deal of spatial overlap in these ranges, the animals also tended to use the same set of trees. However, they generally did not do so at the same time. Mitchell found that 86 per cent of his sightings during the breeding season, and 93 per cent during the non-breeding season, were of animals alone in a tree. Our own observations, covering thousands of individuals in populations living at varying levels of abundance in a range of forest types, show the same picture. Apart from the association between females and their young, the majority of koalas we have seen have been alone. Mammal species in general exhibit a diversity of social organisations, but the solitariness of the koala, as well as the limited time they devote to social interactions, caused Mitchell to conclude that they should be classified as a solitary animal. Most researchers who have conducted long-term field studies on them would concur. Male koalas do not, as some of the old literature suggests, consort with a 'harem' of females, nor does either sex show very much interest in social interaction except of the most basic kind. So do they communicate at all?

SCENT MARKING

In the previous chapter it was shown how the area of the home range that koalas use is largely dictated by the supply of palatable food trees. In habitat where food trees are sparse and widely scattered, such as in central Queensland, koalas range over areas greater than 100 hectares. By comparison Red Bill Creek, the study area where Peter Mitchell worked, was a high quality site with between four and nine koalas to the hectare. This is high-density living for koalas, and Mitchell showed that the males living in this area formed a dominance hierarchy. He suspected that one of the ways they communicated with each other was by scent marking.

One of the main secondary sex characteristics (that is apart from external sex organs) that differentiates male koalas from females is the sternal gland of the males (Figure 5.2). It is a large and odoriferous gland that can be readily seen as a moist, darkly fringed and hairless patch in the middle of the male's chest. Its use, particularly whether it plays any role in spacing behaviour or whether males delineate their ranges with their scent, has often been speculated upon.

Peter Mitchell took up this question and found that adult males (that is over four years old) often marked the trees they were entering. They did this by rubbing their sternum against the trunk or branch they were climbing and smearing their scent for one or two metres along it. They did this most frequently when they were entering unfamiliar trees. Mitchell also noted that these males sometimes dribbled small amounts of urine on the trunks of trees they climbed. Others have often commented on the koala habit of pausing at the base of a tree and sniffing the ground and the tree trunk before climbing it. Mitchell conducted experimental trials to see if sub-dominant males would respond to the freshly smeared scent of a higher-ranking male

Figure 5.2
The sternal (chest) gland is readily visible against the pale fur of this male koala. The gland is used for scent marking.

on the base of a tree they were about to climb. He was not able to detect any consistent response in the sub-dominant animals to this and could not draw any firm conclusions from his trials.

Scent marking and odour obviously play some role in koala society, but there are many apparently contradictory observations, and the precise nature of this role remains to be elucidated. Male koalas, for example, show different patterns of behaviour when approaching other males compared with when they are approaching females and this could be related to their different odours. However, as we will presently describe, males also appear unable to detect whether females are in oestrus, which is surprising as odour is the main cue for detecting oestrus in many other mammalian species.

THE CALL OF THE KOALA

Spreading their odour around is only one of the ways in which koala can potentially communicate with one another. Another is to vocalise. The Australian bush is a fairly quiet place at night and the bellow of a koala is a very unusual noise. Anyone hearing it for the first time is either perplexed about the type of animal making the noise, or just scared witless. Many park rangers can tell stories of being roused in the middle of the night by nervous campers who have fled their tents seeking sanctuary from some diabolical creature growling and roaring at them from the nearby forest. They are usually reassured (and slightly embarrassed) when informed that it 'is just a male koala advertising his presence.

The male call (or bellow) is the one most frequently heard, and it sounds vaguely like the braying of a donkey (Plate 5). It is a sequence of extremely low-pitched sounds: snoring-like inhalations followed by resonant, growling expirations. The sound frequencies range between 0.5 and 5 kilohertz (see Figure 5.3). These are very low frequency sounds compared to the ones usually made by mammals, and have the characteristics of a 'long-range' call. Lower-frequency sounds have an advantage over those of higher frequencies, particularly in heavily forested areas, as they are less attenuated by passing through air and vegetation. Significantly, the low-pitched call of the male koala can be heard from a long distance away, up to a kilometre on a still night.

In many Aboriginal languages the names given to animals are onomatopoeic renditions of their calls. The name for koalas used by the Upper Yarra tribe, a part of the Kulin nation, is 'koob-boor'. Pronounced with the first syllable clipped and the second with a sonorous emphasis ('ku-boooor') it is a fair approximation of the call of the koala.

Figure 5.3
The male bellow is a series of sonorous inhalations and exhalations, and has been likened to that of a donkey. The audiograph (A) shows the inhalations are of short duration (each around 0.5 seconds), with the exhalations longer (around 2 seconds). The power spectrums (B) of representative inhalations and exhalations demonstrate that the inhalations are slightly higher pitched, with a lot more sound energy in the 2–3 kHz range. The sound energy in both phases of the bellow is concentrated below 3 kHz and this low frequency is characteristic of long range calls.

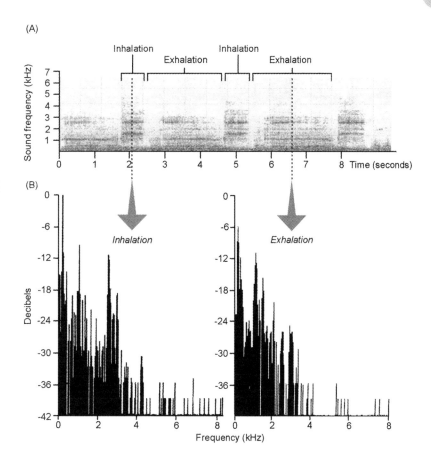

Loud calling by male mammals usually serves the purpose of maintaining distance between individuals, and with koalas the bellowing of the males appears to do this. Peter Mitchell observed that male koalas often bellowed spontaneously after they had changed locations and entered a new tree. He suggested that it was by this means that they communicated their position to neighbouring animals.

Male koalas bellow at all times of the year but they do so more frequently in late spring, when the weather is warming up and their testosterone (the male sex hormone) levels are beginning to rise (see Figure 5.4). Their bellowing heralds the start of the breeding season which continues throughout the summer. In the southern populations, bellowing reaches a crescendo around the end of December, which is the height of the breeding season, but it may peak several weeks earlier in the north.

One chance observation that we made during our field studies suggests that these bellows may play a more significant role than just letting the males know each other's whereabouts. Several years ago we relocated several small groups of koalas from French Island into a 1100 hectare area of open forest and eucalypt plantations at Lysterfield Park near Melbourne. All of the animals were fitted with radio-collars and we kept close track of them. Initially, all of the animals dispersed throughout the park before settling into small home ranges widely separated from each other. One female in particular settled with her dependent young in a range that was some distance away from her nearest neighbour. She resided there for over six months while her young grew to independence. At the start of the next breeding season this female left her young and moved 2.6 kilometres outside of her normal range. When located she was found sharing a tree with an adult male, with another adult male sitting in a tree less than 100 metres from the pair. Both of these males were on the extremities of the ranges they had been occupying for the previous six months. The female subsequently moved back to her original range and, when checked the following month, was found to have a newly-born young in her pouch. Our interpretation of these events was that, following the weaning of her young, the adult female came into oestrus and went searching for a mate. We can not definitely say how she found one but, over such a distance, we believe that the bellowing of the males would have provided a good clue to both their location and inclination.

THE BREEDING SEASON

Koalas breed seasonally, with births occurring between October and May, although the peak period for births may vary between different populations. As the breeding season approaches the levels of reproductive hormones in the blood of males and females rise, with males tending to enter breeding condition a little earlier than the females. The rise in oestradiol and progesterone in females is delayed until their previous seasons young is weaned (see Figures 5.4 and 5.5).

During the breeding season, amid the bellowing chorus of the males, other much higher-pitched calls are heard. They range up to 7 kilohertz in frequency and sound like screams. They are made by female koalas as a response to males attempting to copulate with them. It often seems that the majority of interactions between the sexes in koala society involve the male vigorously attempting to mate the female, while the female appears to be just as vigorous in rebuffing him (see Plate 6). Intermittently the males bellow and the females scream and it is often hard to distinguish whether a fight or a mating is taking place.

Male koalas are considerably larger than females and can usually

Figure 5.4
Testosterone levels in males rise sharply in spring. The seasonal changes in blood plasma testosterone concentrations are shown here for free-ranging male koalas from French Island, Victoria. (From Handasyde *et al.* 1991: values are means; $n = 6$; SE values indicated.)

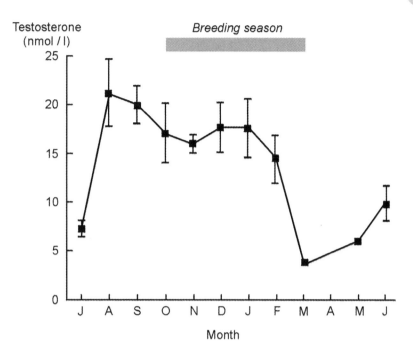

Figure 5.5
Female koalas come into breeding condition later than males, as shown in this graph of seasonal changes in blood plasma oestradiol (solid line) and progesterone (broken line) concentrations in free-ranging female koalas from Phillip Island, Victoria. (Handasyde, unpublished data: values are means; SE ranges indicated; n values are shown above the error bars.)

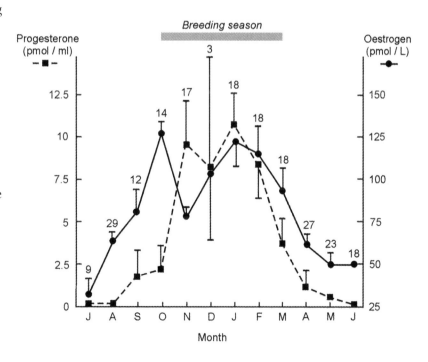

force them into an embrace if they wish to. This embrace usually comes from behind and Peter Mitchell distinguishes between attempted matings and fights by the males' direction of approach. Koalas have relatively uncomplicated personalities and Mitchell noted that when a male was being aggressive rather than amorous he was more likely to simply grasp a female by the elbow and pull her out of the tree.

Female mammals usually display a distinctive set of behaviours when they are in oestrus, and males usually only manage to mount and inseminate receptive females. Experienced handlers of captive koalas can recognise behavioural changes in oestrus females: they show a tendency to incline their heads much further back than usual and are prone to tremors and spasms. Male koalas, however, do not seem to be able to recognise these signs, and field studies indicate that they repeatedly attempted to mount females that are obviously not in oestrus.

Behavioural researchers are not sure of the significance of this, and it may be a further example of koalas' restricted behavioural repertoire, but Peter Mitchell felt that all of the fights, bellows and screams associated with the spring rites of koalas could be seen as part of a fairly robust courtship. Describing such apparent mayhem as 'courtship' seems to be putting a fairly broad interpretation on the word but Mitchell suggested that male koalas, by attempting copulation with all of the females in their area, may be merely 'introducing themselves' to potential mates. Later in the season, when these females eventually come into oestrus, they might not mate randomly but instead submit to one of the males with which they are already familiar.

Mitchell also suggested that the noise accompanying these attempted copulations may play a role in this process of mate selection. All the bellowing and screaming often attracts other adult males from the surrounding area, and the arrival of another male may cause the incumbent to postpone his mating activity in order to fight with him (see Plate 7). The winner of this fight is likely to stay around and thus improve his chances of mating with the female at a later date. Alternatively, such fights may give the female an opportunity to identify which of the males is dominant and this could influence her choice of a mate later in the breeding season.

PREGNANCY AND BIRTH

Female koalas are normally sexually mature from 21 to 24 months of age, but occasionally a precocious female will give birth at around 18 months of age. Gestation lasts about 35 days. It is obvious when a female is in the later stages of pregnancy: the opening of her pouch constricts, and she becomes very sensitive to any interference with it. Her young from the previous season will still be accompanying her and, while it will be almost weaned and feeding mainly on leaves by this time, the mother may still allow it to put its head up to the pouch opening to feed. A new pregnancy, and the hormonal changes it induces, will cause the female to terminate this behaviour and abruptly wean the young.

Old bushmen may tell stories of how they have seen female koalas spank their young when they are at this stage. Ambrose Pratt in the 1930s went to great length describing how an adult female koala he was observing began giving her young an occasional cuffing. Pratt thought it was for disciplinary reasons, but in fact the adult females observed were probably newly pregnant and the cuffing they were handing out to their yearlings was to discourage them from putting their head into a pouch that was being readied for a new occupant.

Koalas normally have a single young each year, although twins are occasionally born. A baby koala, like the young of all other marsupials, is born in a relatively undeveloped state. Known as a 'neonate', it weighs less than 0.5 grams and only has buds for hind limbs (Figure 5.6). It has functional respiratory, digestive and urinary systems as well as strongly muscled shoulders and forelimbs with tiny claws. After emerging from the mother's urogenital opening, the new-born uses these forearms and claws to climb up through the mother's belly fur and enter her pouch. For such a young and poorly developed creature this is truly a miraculous climb. By koala standards its a very short one, but still the most important climb they are ever likely to undertake.

The neonate also has well developed lips and, once inside the pouch, it seeks out the smaller teat, firmly attaches its mouth to it and begins to suck. A female koala has two teats in her pouch (Plate 8) but the young will remain on this same teat throughout its pouch life. By the time it is weaned, this teat will be elongated and flaccid: far too large to accommodate the tiny mouth of the neonate born in the next breeding season. Instead, the new born will attach to the other, smaller teat that has remained unused throughout the previous year.

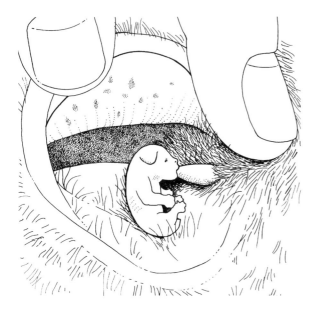

Figure 5.6
The newly born koala neonate attaches itself to a teat inside the mother's pouch. Its miniature size can be clearly seen in relation to human fingers.

MOTHER'S MILK

The composition of koala milk was first studied by Vicki Marshall from the University of Queensland, who found that it differed substantially from the milk of eutherian mammals (such as dogs, horses or humans). When compared to those of eutherian mammals, marsupial milks typically exhibit higher total solids (largely due to very high lipid and protein concentrations), much higher concentrations of some minerals and vitamins (especially iron, retinol, folic and nicotinic acid), and a greater predominance of oligosaccharides other than lactose in the carbohydrate fraction.

Marsupial milk also contrasts with that of eutherian mammals in that it shows quite marked changes in composition over the course of lactation. These changes appear to correspond with the different stages of development of the marsupial young. For example, total carbohydrates in koala milk decrease markedly in late lactation, and this corresponds with weaning when the young are beginning to take in plenty of carbohydrate in the foliage they are eating.

A more comprehensive study of milk production, milk composition and the nutrition of dependant young of free-ranging koalas was undertaken by Andrew Krockenberger from the University of Sydney. Krockenberger found that the composition of koala milk during lactation also differed from the pattern observed in most other marsupials that had been studied. Milk solids decreased at the time of pouch exit, in contrast to the normal pattern in marsupials where the milk becomes more concentrated. Lipids (fats), which provide the major source of energy in milk, did not rise at the time of pouch exit. This contrasts with the pattern in other marsupials, where there is a switch from carbohydrate to lipid as the major source of energy for the emerging young. When he looked at milk production Krockenberger found that, for their size, female koalas had the lowest milk energy production so far recorded in any mammal. However, this was compensated for by the longer lactation period (about 12 months), and he concluded that the low daily rate of energy transfer to the young was yet another consequence of the low nutritive value of the eucalypt diet of their mother. With little energy coming in, there is little to pass on through the milk.

EARLY POUCH LIFE

At the time of birth the koala neonate weighs less than 0.5 grams and has a head length of about 8 millimetres (see Figure 5.6). That this tiny, air-breathing organism will eventually grow into a mature animal weighing as much as 12.5 kilograms, or 25,000 times its birth weight, is one of the more amazing facts of marsupial life history.

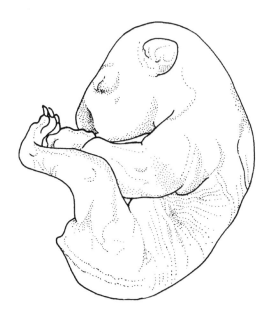

Growth in the early stages of pouch life is relatively rapid. By seven weeks of age (50 days) the head of the pouch-young is 26 millimetres long and disproportionately large compared to the rest its body. The face becomes delineated at this age, with pigmentation appearing on the nose, the eyelids of the still-closed eyes and the edges of the ears (Figure 5.7, and see Plate 9). The sex of the animal is also ascertainable with the male scrotum or the developing female pouch now apparent.

By 13 weeks of age (90 days) the length of the young's head has almost doubled, to 50 mm and its body weight increased to around 50 grams. Until this time the young has been completely naked and still attached to the nipple, but things begin to change from here on. The eyes open for the first time and extremely fine fur begins to appear on the forehead, the nape of the neck, the shoulders and the arms (see 'pelage' in Figure 5.8). By 26 weeks (180 days) the whole body is covered with fur and, for the first time, the baby begins to look like a koala. About this time the young also starts to take an interest in the outside world and occasionally pokes its head out of the pouch, and peeps furtively around.

Figure 5.7
At seven weeks of age the young in the pouch is unfurred, and its eyes are still closed.

Figure 5.8
The stages in the development of a young koala from birth to independence.

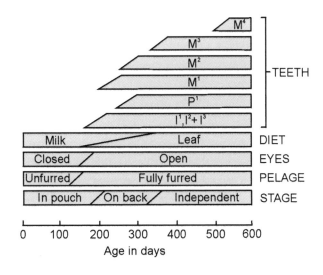

WEANING

As already stated, eucalypt leaves contain a cocktail of chemical compounds that render them unpalatable, if not downright toxic, to most mammals. In these circumstances the commencement of feeding on eucalypt leaves by koalas when they are little more than six months old is a huge gastronomic leap. However the baby will continue to take milk until it is 12 months old.

The preceding chapter noted that, apart from the structure of the gut itself, the micro-organisms which inhabit it appear to be a significant factor in digestion. The process of weaning is initiated when these microbes are introduced into the gut of the young koala. The behavioural sequence by which the female koala passes on to its offspring the ability to digest eucalypt leaves was first reported by Keith Minchin in 1933. He was managing a captive colony of koalas near Adelaide at the time and one day it was drawn to his attention that one of his nursing females appeared to have diarrhoea. The animal otherwise appeared healthy and had a young that was just on the point of emerging from her pouch. When he examined the female, Minchin observed that:

> the head and forearms of the young koala were protruding from the mother's pouch and its face was covered with a yellowish-green slime. The baby was forcing its nose into the mother's cloaca [and] energetically eating the substance from [her] rectum. Although the parent appeared uncomfortable while this was going on, she remained quiet and made no attempt to claw the baby or to stop its activities by moving her position.

Minchin went on to observe that the substance that the young was eating appeared to be pre-digested gum leaves and that judging from the mess on the ground immediately underneath the female, it appeared to have cleared its lower bowel of the normally hard faecal pellets before producing this soft material. The baby koala continued feeding on this 'pap' for almost a month. More detailed observations on this pap feeding were later made by Valerie Thompson on captive koalas held at San Diego Zoo. Her work (Thompson 1987) indicates that it starts when the young is between 172 and 213 days of age, and that the first ingestion of eucalypt leaves usually occurs within 19 days of taking pap.

Keith Minchin was the first to record the impact that ingesting this pap had on the growth and development of young koalas: within two weeks of taking their first meal of pap their body weight almost doubled and they started taking an interest in young gum leaves. By the time they are 12 months old the weaning process is complete and the young koala will be feeding entirely on eucalyptus foliage.

Coprophagy, the ingestion of faeces, is not uncommon in animals and many young eat adult faeces to assist the microbial colonisation of their own gut. Recent analysis of the composition of koala pap by Ro Osawa and his colleagues from the Lone Pine Koala Sanctuary in Queensland showed it to have a very high concentration of the micro-organisms that are normally found in the caecum of the adult koala. As discussed in Chapter 4, this is the main site in the koala gut for the fermentation of leaf digesta and the likely origin of pap. Koalas are therefore not strictly 'coprophagic' as they are not eating faeces. The correct technical term for this is 'caecotrophy'.

DEVELOPMENT OF DENTITION

Eucalyptus leaves are tough, fibrous things to eat and an animal needs an excellent set of teeth to be able to chew them. In her days as veterinarian at the Lone Pine Koala Sanctuary in Queensland, Wendy Blanshard hand-raised a number of koala orphans, whose precise age was known, and closely observed the sequence in which their teeth erupted.

Blanshard found that the first teeth to erupt in the young koala were the incisors: first the lower pair followed shortly after by the two on the upper jaw. These teeth are usually the only ones present when the young enters its caecotrophic stage. Next, the anterior (front) cones of the first molar break through the gum, closely followed by the lower and then the upper premolars. This eruption of the premolars appears to coincide with time that young koalas make their first tentative attempts to chew eucalyptus leaves. The second and third molars follow soon after with the third coming through about the time the animal reaches 12 months of age. The fourth, and final, molar does not appear until the animal is about 18 months old.

LIFE OUTSIDE THE POUCH

The young koala grows rapidly once weaning has commenced and the pouch soon becomes an increasingly restrictive environment for it. Young koalas make their first trip out of the pouch when they are between six and seven months old (180–210 days) and weigh between 300 and 500 grams. On this first journey, the movements of the baby are very tentative. It appears to be very nervous and clings closely to the mother, usually to her chest, as it looks around. In the southern populations this first emergence occurs in late winter, when the weather is often wet and cold, and these early journeys out of the pouch are brief. More extended visits to the outside world occur during the warm, sunny days of early spring.

The young continues to grow rapidly and by the time it reaches 500 grams its fur has adopted the tawny-grey colour of adulthood. By nine months of age (270 days) the young weighs over one kilogram and remains permanently out of the pouch. It no longer needs to enter the pouch to suckle as, by this time, the mother's teat is so elongate that the tip protrudes out through the pouch opening. The young is now more confident in its movements and usually travels around sitting high on the mother's back (Plate 10). It begins making short excursions onto nearby branches and soon becomes adroit at climbing.

When sitting up on its mother's back the young frequently finds itself in among the foliage on which the mother is feeding, and it can often be seen nibbling at the same leaves. As described in Chapter 4, koalas show quite a lot of individual variation in the *Eucalyptus* species on which they feed. One reason for this is that young animals may inherit their mother's food preference as a result of this early exposure. The fact that the young has already has taken 'pap' from the mother at the start of weaning, and thereby derived its gut flora from her, may also be significant in its subsequent feeding preference.

Koalas are excellent mothers and very tolerant of their young, which eventually spend almost three months clinging closely to them. Such intense maternal care is a very successful strategy for the species, and in several populations that we have monitored a high proportion of the young survive to independence. For example, on French Island, Victoria, 100 per cent of the young of a sample of 56 females were successfully weaned. Females that we monitored in another population, in the Brisbane Ranges National Park, Victoria, were less successful but 22 of 25 females (88 per cent) still successfully weaned their young. The three that went missing all disappeared shortly after they first came out of the pouch and we were perplexed for many months about their fate. The mystery was solved when a member of the Geelong Field Naturalists Club told us that the remains of young koalas often turned up under the nearby roost of a pair of powerful owls (*Ninox strenua*) that their group had been monitoring. Feral dogs aside, large owls and possibly wedge-tailed eagles (*Aquila audax*) are probably the only significant predators of young koalas in bushland areas.

INDEPENDENCE

With the warmer weather of the early summer there is a flush of new growth on the eucalypts. This provides an abundance of palatable food for the young koala to eat and it continues to put on weight. It spends more and more time away from its mother's back as it grows, and the close bond between them soon begins to weaken.

The bond is finally broken when the adult female becomes pregnant again. This usually occurs when the young is around 12 months old and weighs about 2.5 kilograms. As described earlier, the newly pregnant female will not permit the young to suckle any more and will give it a good cuffing if it persists in trying to get its head near the pouch opening. Despite this, most young continue to live in close proximity to their mother for the next 6 to 12 months, sharing her range and often feeding in the same tree with her.

Things begin to change when the young approaches 2 years of age. Young females are sexually mature by this time and soon become pregnant. In high abundance populations they are often still living in close proximity to their mother, as well as to the dominant male who probably sired them. These dominant males hold their social position for several years, and we have always suspected that the first mating for some of these two-year-old females may be with their own fathers. However, some recent paternity testing of koalas, conducted by Bill Ellis from the University of Queensland, suggests that these dominant male koalas may not enjoy the mating success that was once thought. Ellis found that a relatively high proportion of the young born in his study population were sired by unidentified, non-resident males. Regardless of who sires them, young females often continue to live in a range adjacent to that of their mother for some years. The majority of young males, however, disperse.

During the breeding season not all of the wailing and screaming comes from adult females protesting the ill-mannered approaches of the males. Young males can also make these distress calls and they do so if they are unfortunate enough to tangle with an adult male. This is often precipitated by the young males themselves who, when approaching sexual maturity, begin to show an interest in neighbouring adult females. If the females become distressed and start to vocalise, this attracts the dominant male who is usually nearby. These males are very aggressive during the breeding season and will fight vigorously with other males, particularly those they find molesting females within their range. Young males are inevitably the losers in these encounters and they wail and sook for some time after a fight. Adult males appear to harass the younger animals even when they are minding their own business. They can be seen together in the same tree, the older animal usually stalking the younger around, with no sign of a female close by. Eventually all this aggression becomes too much for the young males and they depart, presumably looking for some peace in an area that is not occupied by an adult male.

DISPERSAL

The period when naive young animals first leave their mother's home range to make their own way in the world is a hazardous one. When

Ian Eberhard conducted his pioneering field studies on koalas on Kangaroo Island, he felt that dispersing young (particularly males) would experience heavy mortality once they moved from the areas of prime habitat, such as the manna gum (*Eucalyptus viminalis*) forests where they were born, to more marginal habitat. It is very difficult to keep track of dispersing animals and at the time Ian Eberhard had no way of testing his hypothesis. (His field study was conducted in the late 1960s and at that time the technology of using miniature radio-transmitters to keep track of wildlife was in its infancy.)

A decade later, when small radio-transmitters for wildlife studies were commonplace, Peter Mitchell monitored the fate of 44 koalas that were born on his study site at Red Bill Creek. He found that a high proportion (88 per cent) of the males emigrated when they were between two and three years old, whereas a lower proportion of the females (51 per cent) did so. The 49 per cent of the females that remained were still in the study area at the end of the study, by which time they were over 4.5 years old. A relatively small number of the dispersing animals (both males and females) died. Most survived and wandered about for a year or two. For an arboreal animal that is normally regarded as sedentary, Mitchell found that koalas had surprising powers of dispersal when they put their minds to it. One of his study animals moved over 8 kilometres in a 6-week period. Eventually all of the dispersing group settled at scattered localities across the island, some of them in surprisingly poor habitat.

SEXUAL AND PHYSICAL MATURITY

As stated above, female koalas are sexually mature and capable of having their first young when they are between 21 and 24 months of age. Body weight appears to be as good a criterion as age in assessing sexual maturity, and females from southern populations, which are significantly larger than those from the north, are capable of breeding as soon as they attain a body weight of 6 kilograms.

The onset of sexual maturity in males is a little more complex. Males are capable of producing viable sperm as two-year-olds, and in low-abundance populations possibly mate with females at this age. In high-abundance populations, however, they are unlikely to get access to females at this age as they do not have the body mass to compete with the big boys in the free-for-all that is the koala breeding season. For them to mate successfully, they would need to be very sneaky about it and be lucky enough to find a compliant and very quiet female. Most of them probably have limited mating success until they are big enough to hold their ground against a mature adult. In southern populations, this means they must reach a body weight in excess

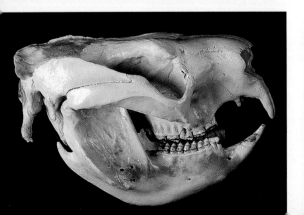

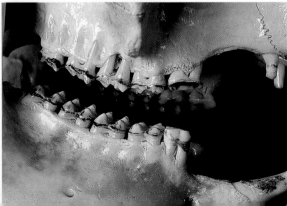

Plate 4
Typical koala
habitat. Woodland
in the Brisbane
Ranges National
Park, Victoria,
containing a
mixed stand of
eucalypt species.
(Kath Handasyde)

Plate 5
The typical
posture of a
male koala when
bellowing.
(Peter Fell)

Plate 6
Female koalas
do not always
appreciate
attention from
males during the
breeding season,
and sometimes
aggressively rebuff
them. (Peter Fell)

**Plate 7
a, b, c & d**
Adult male koalas commonly fight with each other during the breeding season. There is nothing ritualised about these fights and they often result in injuries which contribute to the shorter life expectancy of males. Not all of this male-male combat occurs in trees, as this series of photographs shows. (7a Peter Fell; 7b, c & d Kath Handasyde)

Plate 8
The pouch of
an adult female
koala showing the
two nipples. The
elongated nipple
is being used by a
large back-young
approaching
independence.
When the new
season's young is
born it will attach
to the unused,
smaller nipple.
(Roger Martin)

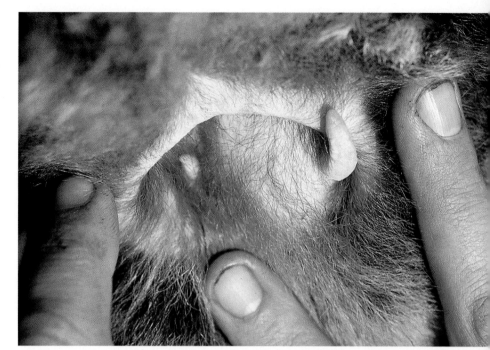

Plate 9
A two to three
month old koala
pouch-young.
At this stage the
baby is still naked
and the eyes
permanently
closed. The dark
pigmentation and
characteristic
shape of the
nose give the
baby a distinctively
koala-like
appearance
even at this
early age.
(Roger Martin)

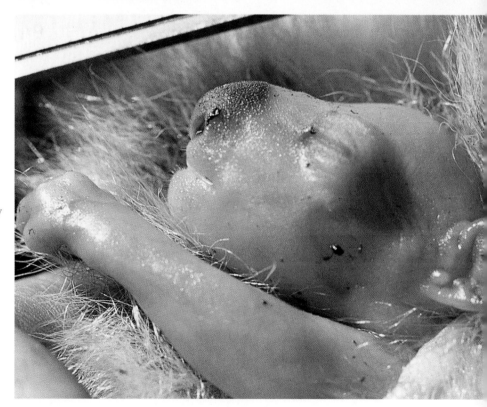

Plate 10
Young koalas ride on their mother's back from about nine months of age. This 12-month-old back-young is fully weaned and a competent climber, but young at this age may still hitch a ride on their mothers occasionally. (Peter Fell)

Plate 11
Infection of the eye with *Chlamydia* can cause keratocon-junctivitis ('pink-eye') in koalas. Less than three per cent of animals in wild Victorian populations are affected by this disease. (Kath Handasyde)

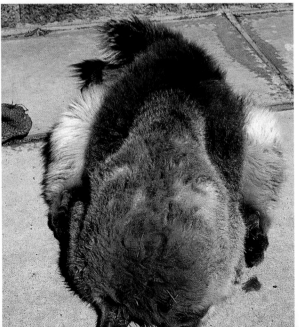

Plate 12
Urinary tract infections with *Chlamydia* result in the debilitating disease known as 'dirty-tail or 'wet-bottom' in koalas. Advanced cases of 'dirty-tail' cannot be treated and result in the death of the animal. (Kath Handasyde)

Plate 13
All things vertical are not trees. Urban development causes a range of problems for koalas. (Kath Handasyde)

Plate 14
Female koala in a defoliated manna gum on French Island, Victoria. The high fertility rate of the French Island koalas has led to over-population and the consequent heavy browsing pressure on food trees has been a problem for many decades. (Roger Martin)

Plate 15
The consequences of too many koalas. In the late 1990s, at Framlingham Bush in western Victoria, the koalas increased to such high numbers that they defoliated and killed the manna gum forest on which they depended. As a result of the food shortage the population crashed with thousands of koalas starving to death. (Roger Martin)

Plate 16
Highly fecund koala populations degrade small patches of forest relatively quickly. At Sandy Point, Western Port, Victoria, a population which started with 20 *Chlamydia*-free koalas in 1972, increased so rapidly that it had killed nearly 200 hectares of food trees by 1988. (Kath Handasyde)

of 12 kilograms. Normally Victorian male koalas do not achieve this until they are at least 4 years of age.

LONGEVITY

One question commonly asked by members of the general public about a wildlife species is 'How long do they live?'. If a species is relatively long lived (that is living more than 10 years) field biologists usually can not give a precise answer to the question unless there have been long-term field studies conducted on a single population. (These days the average duration of a field study on a native Australian mammal would be less than 5 years.) As with many of the more intimate details of the life of wild species, we have to rely on the information collected from the captive individuals held in zoos and wildlife sanctuaries. Life in captivity is by no means equivalent to life in the wild. If the husbandry is of a high standard, animals in captivity can live much longer than they otherwise would. Often, however, the longevity estimates based on captive data are the best we have.

In a survey conducted in 1987 of the 17 Australian institutions then holding koalas in captivity, the oldest animal was at least 15 years old and animals between 10 and 13 years old were not uncommon. The longevity record for a captive animal appears to be 18 years, held by a female kept at San Diego Zoo in the United States.

Limited data on wild animals from a population at Walkerville in South Gippsland, suggests that potential longevity of koalas in the wild is similar to that suggested by the captive records. One female, first captured in August 1977 and adjudged by the extent of the wear on her teeth to be at least 5 years old, was recaptured in February 1990, when she must then have been at least 18 years old. Another female, first captured at the same study site as a two-year-old in 1978, was still breeding when recaptured as a 12-year-old. In the Brisbane Ranges study population the super-mum 'Blue/Blue' lived until she was 18 years old, and bred until she was over 13 years old.

Perhaps the most detailed records on the longevity of free-living koalas are those held by the Koala Preservation Society of New South Wales. This society, which is based at Port Macquarie, has struggled for many years to conserve their local koalas in the face of the increasing urbanisation of the area. Among their many activities they run a Koala Hospital and they tag and keep detailed records of all of the koalas that pass through it. They have records of several animals in this population, both male and female, that have survived to 18 years of age.

Taken together, all the records suggest that females commonly live between 13 and 18 years in the wild. While capable of reaching the same old age as females, the life of males is more hazardous and their life expectancy appears to be considerably shorter.

TOOTH WEAR, AGEING AND AGE DETERMINATION

When the absolute age of a koala is not known, and with most wild animals it isn't, it is important to have some method of assessing relative age. In veterinary medicine, for example, it is useful to have some idea of the animals age in both the diagnosis of an illness and the prognosis of any treatment. Advanced age may limit an animal's ability to recover from illness or injury. Some assessment of the age structure of koala populations is also very important for management purposes, particularly for understanding the dynamics of the population, but we will deal with that in Chapter 8.

The cheek teeth of the koala comprise a single premolar and four molars on each side of the upper and lower jaws. This is the animal's lifetime complement of teeth and all have erupted by the time it is 18 months old. After this, there are no more new teeth, just continual wear on the occlusal (biting or grinding) surfaces of the existing ones. This continues until the enamel on the cutting ridges and pyramidal cusps is worn away. The underlying dentine is then exposed and the characteristic wear patterns that appear can be used to assign the animal to an age class. There are seven of these classes and they and the approximate chronological ages they represent are shown in Figure 5.9.

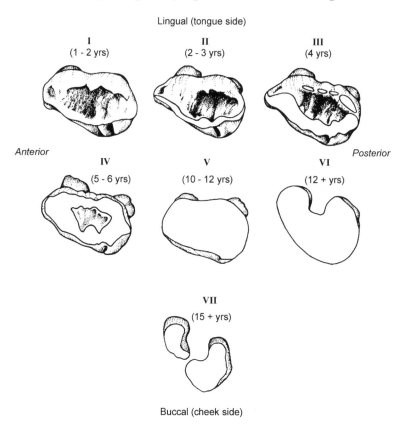

Figure 5.9
The characteristic wear patterns on a premolar from the upper jaw of a koala can be used to assess the age of the animal. (After Martin 1981.)

PREDATORS, PARASITES AND PATHOGENS

The focus of the preceding chapters has largely been on the behavioural and life history traits of the koala. These are the inherent characteristics of the species. However, in order to discuss the important question of conservation status and of the ability of the koala to 'survive in the wild', it is necessary to look at koalas collectively; that is, as populations.

The 'population' is the basic unit that wildlife managers deal with, and population biology is now an important area in wildlife conservation. The basic equation of survival is that a population will persist in the wild if the annual total of new recruits (births and immigrants) equals or exceeds losses due to deaths and emigration. Immigration and emigration (young adult koalas dispersing to new home ranges) were discussed in Chapter 5, and birth rate is dealt with in the next chapter. This part of the discussion considers the major factors which act to decrease population numbers. While some wild animals die of old age, most either succumb to disease or are killed by predators.

PREDATORS AND MISADVENTURE

Over its long evolutionary history, the koala has undoubtedly been killed and eaten by a diverse array of predators. In the rainforests of the Miocene lurked *Thylacoleo* — a leopard-sized, semi-arboreal marsupial with sabre-like premolars that, according to some palaeontologists, was capable of capturing and making a meal of an arboreal species such as a koala. Large pythons also prey on arboreal animals and the now extinct *Wonambi naracoortensis* probably shared the ancient rainforests with koalas and consumed the odd one or two. The recently extinct Tasmanian tiger or thylacine (*Thylacinus cynocephalus*) occurred on the Australian mainland until 3300 years ago and, while it could not climb trees, it would have been able to kill koalas when they came to the ground. The thylacine was progressively displaced on the mainland by the dingo (*Canis lupus dingo*) from about 4000 years ago. The dingo was probably a far more agile predator and would have been an efficient killer of koalas, particularly any it caught on the ground while they were moving between trees.

The dingo appears to have been first introduced to Australia as a semi-domesticated hunting companion by an even more adept hunter, *Homo sapiens*. Evidence from a number of sources suggests a human presence in Australia for anywhere from 60, 000 to over 100, 000 years and the impact of hunting on the abundance of koalas by both indigenous Australians, and the white 'pelt-shooters' that subsequently displaced them, has been discussed in Chapter 2.

These days the main killers of koalas, particularly of animals in semi-urban areas, appear to be those modern-day human appendages, the domestic dog and the motor car. Large dogs are exceedingly popular in suburban Australia, and they kill many koalas that wander into backyards. Motor cars and trucks probably account for a lot more, and a high level of road-kills are a problem for many koala populations in urbanised areas. Interstate expressways passing through rural areas also account for a large number of animals. Along Highway 31, north of Melbourne, you pass many silhouette signs warning of koalas crossing the road, yet carcasses always litter the verge.

In bushland areas, away from the freeways and domestic dogs, the koala now has few natural enemies. As has already been related, powerful owls (*Ninox strenua*) may occasionally take small young off female koalas' backs, as we suspect happened at our Brisbane Ranges study site. At the same site, wedge-tailed eagles (*Aquila audax*) occasionally came down to inspect us closely when we were up in the canopy catching koalas. Eagles are reported to take koalas, and they certainly look capable of doing so, but no one has documented it. In some areas packs of feral dogs may be a problem, but overall the koala is relatively free of predators.

Another, not uncommon cause of mortality for koalas is misadventure. Despite their noted ability to survive falls, sometimes from surprising heights, koalas occasionally injure themselves when they fall. In forests where koalas are common, you occasionally come across the carcass of a freshly dead animal lying under a tree. Often the only apparent cause of death is a fall. Sometimes the bodies are of young animals, that probably fall because they are inexperienced climbers and make mistakes. An adult's fall can be caused by little more than a sudden gust of wind swaying the branch and dislodging the 'always-sleeping' koala from its fork. Most times they get up, look around and then slowly climb back up the same tree. Occasionally, however, they are mortally injured. Injuries and deaths from falls are probably more common among males as a result of them fighting with each other. We suspect this is one of the main reasons that average life expectancy among male koalas is lower than that of females.

PARASITES

The natural world is not a benign place and all wild things have their own quota of parasites and pathogens. Parasites are organisms that live on or in a host species and make a living from it. Some parasites do not appear to harm their host, particularly when they are in low numbers. Other parasites always harm their hosts, particularly when their numbers get very high.

Koalas generally have relatively few intestinal parasites: for example, they host only one tapeworm species, *Bertiella obesa*. Small numbers of adult tapeworms are common in the small intestine of the koala and appear to be harmless to the host. Heavy burdens (infestations) are debilitating and render the host weak and lethargic, and possibly more susceptible to predators or other pathogens.

Surprisingly, koalas are also relatively free of the more common external parasites of mammals, such as lice and fleas, but ticks are a problem in some coastal areas. In coastal South Gippsland, Victoria, most koalas seem to carry a few specimens of the tick species *Ixodes tasmani* attached to the edge of their ears. The life cycle of this tick requires the female to have a blood meal before it can breed and, because they concentrate the blood as they feed, it may take 5 millilitres of the host's blood before a tick is engorged. Exsanguination (severe loss of blood) as a result of a heavy tick burden can cause mortality in koalas.

The paralysis tick *Ixodes holocyclus* infests coastal koala populations further north. It also occurs in Victoria, particularly in the eastern corner of the state, and it is deadly to koalas with no previous exposure and thus no immunity to the tick's toxin. Several years ago a number of koalas relocated to this area from further south all died as a result of infestations by *I. holocyclus*.

There are another two particularly nasty external parasites that koalas suffer from, but fortunately neither are common. One is mange, a condition caused by a tiny mite *Sarcoptes scabiei* as it burrows into and feeds on the skin of its host. It is a scourge in common wombats but only occasionally reported in koalas. The other unpleasant condition is caused by the bacterium *Mycobacterium ulcerans*. This bacterium is related to the organism that causes leprosy in humans. In koalas, *M. ulcerans* causes large skin ulcers that will not heal and are extremely difficult to treat.

A range of parasitic micro-organisms are known to infect koalas. The yeast-like fungus *Crypotcoccus neoformans* causes a respiratory disease that can lead to sudden death in a range of marsupials, including koalas. There appears to be a fascinating but only partially understood ecological relationship involving this fungus, two important food species of the koala, the river and forest red gums (*Eucalyptus camaldulensis* and *E. tereticornis*), and possibly the koala itself. The two tree species are the only known hosts of the variety of the fungus designated *C. neoformans gatti* which shed large amounts of sexual propagules (basidiospores) into the environment when the trees flower. The fungus has been isolated from swabs taken from the paws of koalas, from their fresh faeces and from the foliage they were feeding upon, but whether koalas can be regarded as a carrier of the fungal cells (as the pigeon is postulated to be for the other variety of *C. neoformans*, var. *neoformans*) is yet to be elucidated.

PATHOGENS

Autopsy results and veterinary reports collected over a number of years from both captive and free-living animals indicate that koalas are particularly susceptible to opportunistic infections, such as *Cryptococcus*. (Opportunistic infections are ones that usually display low pathogenicity and are easily dealt with by the immune system of a healthy host. They only develop into disease in debilitated animals or those whose immune system is somehow compromised.) Koalas show a higher than expected incidence of lymphoid cancer and leukaemia, and it has been suggested that their apparent susceptibility may be due the presence of a retrovirus. Retroviruses act to impair the effectiveness of their host's immune system. The human disease AIDS (Acquired Immune Deficiency Syndrome), for example, is caused by a retrovirus. In 1988, virus particles that morphologically resembled a retrovirus were observed in the bone marrow of a koala that had been diagnosed with leukaemia and retrovirus activity was subsequently demonstrated in cultures grown from koala white blood cells (lymphocytes). Retrovirus infections are suspected to play a role in koalas' susceptibility to disease, but the precise nature of that role is yet to be demonstrated.

CHLAMYDIAL INFECTION IN KOALA POPULATIONS

One group of pathogenic micro-organisms that are widely considered to be opportunistic are bacteria belonging to the family Chlamydiae. On present knowledge, they are the most significant pathogen of koalas.

The root word for the name of this group, 'chlamys', is derived from the Greek and means 'cloaked' or 'hidden'. It is a fitting description for these most elusive of micro-organisms. They are relatively primitive and live inside the cells of their host where they hijack the cell's energy-rich compounds for their own metabolic and reproductive needs.

There are essentially two phases in the chlamydial cycle of cell invasion and multiplication (see Figure 6.1). In the first they take the form of an 'elementary body' (EB), which is a cocoon-shaped particle about 300 nanometres in diameter (1 nanometre is one millionth of a metre). This particle is specialised for life outside the cell. It is taken into a host cell by a process known as 'phagocytosis': essentially it sticks itself to the outside of the cell and the cell envelops it. Once inside, the EB doubles its size and becomes somewhat spherical in shape. In this form it is known as a 'reticulate body' (RB). This RB replicates itself many times, each generation becoming smaller until they resume the appearance of EBs. This all happens while they are enclosed in a vacuole within the cytoplasm of the cell, but eventually this vacuole bursts, the cell ruptures and a large number of new EBs are released. These infect adjoining cells and thus the cycle begins again. The entry point of *Chlamydia* into a 'naive' (previously unexposed) host is usually via tissue with a moist surface layer of epithelial cells, the sort of tissue commonly encountered in reproductive tracts, eye sockets, nasal passages and lungs. Once infection is established, the proliferation of damaged cells soon develops an obvious lesion in the tissue.

Figure 6.1
The life cycle of *Chlamydia*.

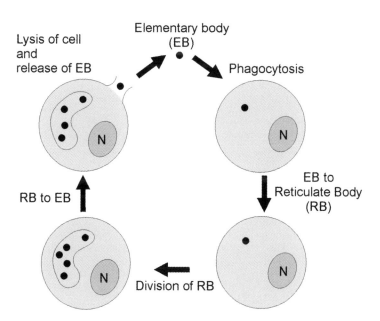

Elementary body (EB)

Lysis of cell and release of EB

Phagocytosis

RB to EB

EB to Reticulate Body (RB)

Division of RB

Koalas have long been known to be susceptible to eye disease. In 1937 Noel Burnett, an early student of koalas, was reportedly pessimistic about the future of the wild populations in Queensland largely because diseases such as 'ophthalmia and conjunctivitis' were so prevalent. A few years later Ellis Troughton, then Curator of Mammals at the Australian Museum in Sydney, attributed the deaths of millions of koalas at around the turn of the century to 'some form of ophthalmic disease'. Troughton went on to state that these epidemics resulted from disease 'introduced as a result of settlement'. He produced no evidence to support this view but, in the light of some recent research, his statement may yet prove to be prescient.

The first evidence linking eye disease in koalas with *Chlamydia* was presented in 1974 by two veterinarians, Frank Cockram and Alan Jackson. They had noticed that an acute form of conjunctivitis, known as keratoconjunctivitis or 'pink-eye', was prevalent in wild koalas in northern New South Wales. The conjunctiva is the area of sensitive skin beneath the eye-lid, and in animals suffering from 'pink-eye' this area becomes enlarged, inflamed and granular (see Plate 11). In acute cases, the conjunctiva has a pink cauliflower-like appearance and protrudes out from the eye margins. In their study, Cockram and Jackson observed that in some populations up to 29 per cent of animals were clinically affected. In seeking the agent responsible they were able to culture *Chlamydia*, which they identified as *C. psittaci*, from 29 of 35 koalas suffering from keratoconjunctivitis. Subsequent studies of this disease have shown that in the worst cases it can lead to ulceration of the cornea and result in blindness in one or both eyes. In our own studies, where wild populations have been monitored over several years, we have seen a number of animals recover fully from mild cases of 'pink-eye'.

Evidence linking *Chlamydia* with reproductive tract disease in koalas appeared ten years after Cockram and Jackson's results were published. At the time, our research group had been gathering data on fertility rates from a number of Victorian populations. There were large differences in the fertility rates of the populations and we could not explain why. The differences in reproductive output between the koala populations on French and Phillip Islands, two large islands adjacent to each other in Western Port, were particularly outstanding. The vegetation and general habitat for koalas were broadly similar on both islands. If anything Phillip Island had larger trees and more fertile soil, yet only 17 per cent of the sexually mature females on Phillip Island were breeding compared with 97 per cent on French Island. In seeking an explanation for this, we enlisted the aid of a couple of veterinarians then working at the Veterinary Research Institute in Melbourne, Ken McColl and Laurie Gleeson. A number of potential disease organisms were screened for, but the results obtained when testing for the presence of *Chlamydia* were unequivocal. Using an antibody test on blood samples we collected from animals in both populations, McColl and Gleeson found that 98 per cent of the Phillip Island animals had high antibody levels to *Chlamydia*, compared with only 7 per cent of those on French Island.

A subsequent investigation conducted by another veterinarian, David Obendorf, found pathological changes to the reproductive tracts of female koalas from Phillip Island. The gross changes he observed included enlargement of the fallopian tubes and cystic dilation of the ovarian bursae (the bursae being purse-like structures that envelop the ovaries). Sometimes these cysts were as large as oranges and extended down into the fallopian tubes. Obendorf considered the whole syndrome to be a chronic sequel to the inflammatory processes accompanying an ascending infection of the reproductive tract. Reproductive tract disease and infertility were well-known consequences of chlamydial infection in females from a number of species, including our own. (In human females the syndrome is known as pelvic inflammatory disease.) Combining the studies of McColl, Gleeson and Obendorf implicated *Chlamydia* as the major cause of infertility in female koalas on Phillip Island.

Shortly after this, a research group working in Queensland led by another veterinarian, Steve Brown, confirmed this association of *Chlamydia* with both conjunctivitis and reproductive tract disease in koalas. This group also reported another two disease syndromes in koalas that were caused by *Chlamydia*. One was a disease of the respiratory tract (causing rhinitis and pneumonia) and the other a urinary tract infection that was mainly found in females. The latter disease leads to incontinence and it became known as 'dirty-tail' or 'wet-bottom' because of the permanently wet, matted and stinking fur surrounding the rump of the animal (see Plate 12). This infection can involve the bladder and spread up the ureters to the kidneys. It debilitates and eventually kills the animal.

Surveys of the prevalence of *Chlamydia* in wild populations were subsequently conducted in South Australia, Victoria, New South Wales and Queensland. With the exception of two artificially established populations, one on French Island (Victoria) and the other on Kangaroo Island (South Australia), all of the other populations tested showed evidence of diseases caused by *Chlamydia*. The syndromes 'pink-eye' and 'dirty-tail' were not especially prevalent — less than 3 per cent of animals showed any evidence of infection. However, all of the infected populations exhibited reduced fertility, with between 17 and 66 per cent of females breeding at any one site. Infertility, caused by reproductive tract disease in females, appeared to be the most serious impact of *Chlamydia* on koala populations. Subsequent monitoring of male animals from infected populations indicated that they also had chlamydial infections in their urogenital tracts. It appeared to cause some inflammation but no serious pathology was detected. However, later trials indicated that infected male koalas could transmit *Chlamydia* to females by sexual contact.

Research conducted by Martin Lavin and his students at the Queensland Institute of Medical Research shed further light on what was rapidly becoming a very complex story. Using the techniques of molecular biology, Lavin's group were able to compare DNA extracted from *Chlamydia* isolated from different sites of infection in the koala. They found that the DNA of *Chlamydia* isolated from the eye was readily distinguishable from that obtained from the reproductive tract. This was the first evidence that koalas were infected with more than one strain of *Chlamydia* and these strains became known as Type I (ocular) and Type II (urogenital). Another completely unexpected result of this work was the discovery that there was a surprising degree of similarity in the profiles of the koala Type II (urogenital) strain and a *Chlamydia* isolated from lung tissue of diseased cattle.

Concurrent with this work by Australian scientists to identify the strains of *Chlamydia* infecting koalas, overseas scientists were revising the taxonomy of the whole Chlamydiae group. At the time the first *Chlamydia* was isolated from koalas, by Frank Cockram and Alan Jackson in 1974, only two species were recognised. One, *C. trachomatis*, was thought to cause disease in humans and the other, *C. psittaci*, to be a pathogen of the remainder of the animal kingdom. At the time *C. psittaci* was thought to be one of the most ubiquitous species of micro-organisms on earth and, besides koalas, had been isolated from a diverse group of hosts including birds, mammals, frogs and even insects. One strain of *C. psittaci* was thought responsible for an epidemic of human respiratory disease in the late 1800s, but the organism was thought to have originated in infected cage birds. However, in 1989 a *Chlamydia* responsible for a human respiratory infection was found to differ so significantly from *C. psittaci* that it was described as a new species, *C. pneumoniae*. In 1993, molecular biologists comparing the DNA of this new species with that of the koala ocular strain (*C. psittaci* Type I) found such a high degree of similarity that they suggested that the latter was in fact a strain of *C. pneumoniae*. In the same year a fourth species of the genus, *C. pecorum*, was described. Subsequent work reported a high degree of similarity between the genetic make-up of this new species and that of the koala urogenital strain (*C. psittaci* Type II). The current thinking on the genus is summarised in Figure 6.2.

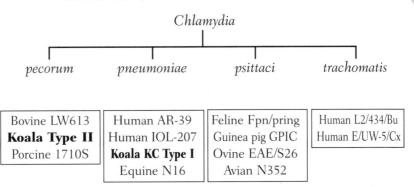

Figure 6.2
Current
taxonomy of
Chlamydia.
These are the
postulated
relationships
between the
various species
and strains of
Chlamydia,
based on
homology of
mapped
sequences
in DNA.
(Modified from
Blanshard 1994.)

The most recent developments in our understanding of *Chlamydia* in koalas have come from the work of Peter Timms and his students at the Queensland University of Technology. The story remains complex. At the present time, it is believed that the koala can become infected by a number of strains of *Chlamydia* from two distinct species. The first group, *C. pneumoniae*, appears to have a preference for ocular sites while the second, *C. pecorum*, can cause both ocular and urogenital infections. Further genetic analysis of a number of cultures of *C. pecorum* isolated from koalas revealed eight distinct strains. The significance of this is as yet unclear, but some of these strains are genetically very similar to *Chlamydia* isolated from domestic animals and it is now being suggested that at least some of the original *C. pecorum* infections in koalas may have resulted from cross-species transmissions from pigs, sheep and cattle.

In the light of this work it is interesting to recall those early accounts that spoke of epidemics of 'some form of ophthalmic disease' that caused the deaths of millions of koalas, and the view of the late Ellis Troughton that these had resulted from disease 'introduced as a result of settlement'. The status of the other koala strains that appear to be unrelated to those found in domestic animals is as yet unclear. They may prove to be a *Chlamydia* unique to the koala and one that has been in a long-established 'host/parasite' relationship with them. If this is the case, then it may explain the comparatively benign impact of *Chlamydia* on some koala populations.

THE EFFECTS OF *CHLAMYDIA* ON KOALA POPULATIONS

Our understanding of *Chlamydia* taxonomy has proceeded very rapidly over the last few years and no doubt, with the increasingly powerful tools available to molecular biologists, it will continue to advance. Our understanding of the impact of *Chlamydia* on koalas at the population level, however, has lagged. Hopefully it will proceed more rapidly now that we can distinguish the different strains of the bacterium. Surveys that we conducted in the mid-1980s across south-eastern Australia showed that fertility rates were not uniform across *Chlamydia*-infected populations (see Chapter 7). So far, we have only been able to speculate why this is so. It may be because there are a number of chlamydial strains involved and each has a different virulence, infects different organs, and causes different degrees of pathological damage. But its impact also has something to do with a population's history of exposure to *Chlamydia*.

Reviewing the history of koalas on French Island we can be fairly confident that they have existed in an environment free from any urogenital strain (Type II) of *Chlamydia* for around 100 years. The few positive results in surveys for *Chlamydia* antibodies conducted on the island indicate that the koalas there have some exposure to *Chlamydia* but it apparently is not a particularly virulent or pathogenic strain as there is no evidence of disease. However, we know that when these naive French Island animals come into contact with the strain of *Chlamydia* that is present in some mainland populations, it has dire consequences, particularly for the fertility of the females. We first became aware of this when monitoring a small group of koalas relocated from French Island to Phillip Island. At the time translocation was being investigated as an option for boosting the declining koala population of Phillip Island and we tracked the reproductive success of these translocated females for several years. We found that it declined rapidly, with only a few females producing young after their first breeding season on the island and none at all in the second. Autopsies conducted on some of these females revealed lesions in the reproductive tract similar to those previously described by David Obendorf as the sequel to *Chlamydia* infection. Subsequent to this, we had a sobering demonstration of the impact of *Chlamydia* when it was introduced to a large population of naive animals in the Grampians National Park in western Victoria.

There is some evidence of an endemic population of koalas in the Grampians as late as 1938 but they are believed to have been wiped out by bushfires shortly after this time. As part of an early program to rehabilitate the koala in Victoria, a small group of koalas of Phillip Island origin were released into a contained area in the Grampians in 1947 (Figure 6.3). This contained area was a small island, Wartook Island, in the middle of an artificial lake, Lake Wartook. This population was monitored regularly and grew slowly, with small groups being moved off whenever the trees were showing any sign of defoliation as a result of the browsing pressure. In most of these population reduction exercises, the koalas were transported and released at sites some distance away from the Grampians. However, in 1963, 20 of these koalas were released into the bush around the shoreline of Lake Wartook. From here they presumably dispersed into the surrounding forest.

Figure 6.3
The history of koala translocations into the Grampians region of Victoria, where *Chlamydia* was inadvertently introduced into a large population of naive animals.

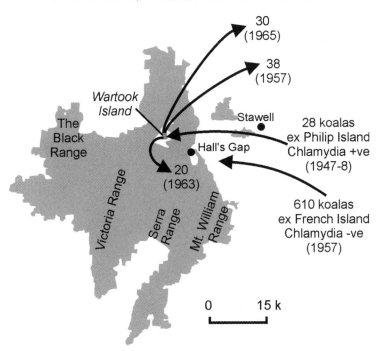

Several years before this, in 1957, another, much larger group of more than 600 koalas had been released into the Grampians. These animals came from French Island and most of them were released in the Halls Gap area, which is about ten kilometres from Lake Wartook. Initially this group thrived, as French Island koalas often do, and koala numbers began to increase alarmingly in the Halls Gap area. Sometime after this, breeding tapered off and 25 years later, when we conducted an early summer survey of the area to count the number of females with back young, we sighted 110 koalas but saw only a single female carrying a young. A subsequent survey confirmed the poor reproductive performance of this population and antibody tests for the presence of *Chlamydia* showed that 84 per cent of the Halls Gap koalas were positive. A follow-up survey a few years later gave the same result. Reproduction has remained low since that time and koala numbers have declined to the point where they are now thought of as a relatively rare animal around Halls Gap.

The circumstantial evidence, based on the Phillip Island origin and low rate of increase of the Wartook Island animals, suggests that they were infected with a urogenital strain of *Chlamydia* at the time they were first released. It is probable that the small group subsequently relocated from there into the Grampians introduced the bacteria into the Halls Gap population. The Halls Gap animals, being of French Island origin and having no prior exposure to the urogenital strain of *Chlamydia*, had little resistance to it and were severely affected. An extremely low rate of fertility (first noted in 1986 but probably present for some years prior to this) resulted, and the consequent low birth rate of this population has led to its gradual decline to the present day.

The history of the Grampians population illustrates two points about *Chlamydia* and its impact on koala populations. One is that populations that are naive, particularly to the urogenital strain, are extremely susceptible to it. On first contact a large proportion of females in such a population will be rendered permanently infertile. This has dire implications for the population and the wide-scale collapse of koala populations reported by Ellis Troughton in the late 1800s and early 1900s may well have been an example of naive populations encountering a new stain of *Chlamydia* and being overwhelmed by it.

The second point is that koalas eventually do mount an effective immune response to *Chlamydia* and some female koalas are able to continue breeding despite the fact that their reproductive tract is infected. We do not know precisely how they manage to do this, but from studies on other species (including our own) we know that the immunological response of a population to a new pathogenic organism is gradually enhanced over time. On first exposure most animals succumb, with only a small number (often a very small number) remaining healthy. It may be purely by chance that this happens or it may be that some of animals have already been exposed to a less pathogenic strain of a related organism and developed a prior immunity. Or it may be genetic, with the odd, rare individual being naturally immune. It may also be that, on first exposure, a few otherwise healthy animals receive such a low dose of the new pathogen that their immune systems cope sufficiently for them to resist it.

However it is acquired, this immunity is passed on to offspring (usually via antibodies, either in their milk or possibly even across the placenta while the young is still in utero). In this way the overall immune competence of a population is slowly enhanced and succeeding generations are better able to deal with the parasite. Over the longer term, populations are said to develop a 'balanced host-parasite relationship' with parasites and this seems to have happened with *Chlamydia* in many mainland koala populations. In these, a significant number of female koalas continue to breed despite having *Chlamydia*. These populations never achieve the same level of fecundity as *Chlamydia*-free ones, but they still have a positive rate of increase. The Grampians population appears to still be in a phase of low numbers but, given enough time, and barring other catastrophic events, it may recover.

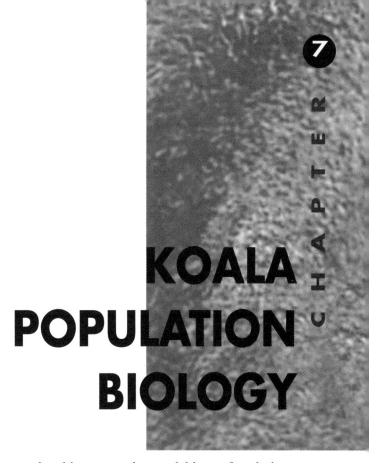

KOALA POPULATION BIOLOGY

CHAPTER 7

Members of the general public are understandably confused about the status of koalas in the wild because the situation is complex. Many people believe that the koala is a rare and threatened species, and in the recent past in some areas, it has been. There have been local extinctions and such extinctions are still possible, even today. At the same time koalas are abundant in many areas, so abundant in some that they are defoliating and killing their food trees. This chapter examines the apparent paradox of both these situations being simultaneously true with a discussion of koala population biology.

Population biology is a large and complex subject. It is mainly concerned with the underlying factors that cause a population to change its size. Contrary to what many people think, the number of individuals in a population of wild animals is not static: in fact, it is very unusual for numbers in such populations to remain constant over time. Fluctuations are driven by demographic changes (that is changes in the rates of birth, death, immigration and emigration), with environmental conditions, particularly severe climatic changes such as drought or unseasonable cold and wet weather, usually having the overriding influence. Catastrophes, such as bushfires or the arrival of new pathogens, can have a substantial impact on birth and death rates and result in a rapid change in a populations size.

Catastrophes aside, natality (birth) rates have a far more significant impact on the rate of increase of a population. Things are seldom straight forward when it comes to natality, and with koalas there is the complicating factor of *Chlamydia*. The impact of *Chlamydia* on the fertility of individual females, and its impact on naive populations has already been described, and its impact on populations with a more balanced 'host-parasite' relationship is covered later in the chapter. The benchmark against which these situations may be measured is a naturally fecund, *Chlamydia*-free population.

CHLAMYDIA-FREE POPULATIONS

THE HISTORY OF THE KOALA POPULATION ON FRENCH ISLAND, VICTORIA

French Island has played a prominent role in the development of our understanding of the dynamics of koala populations, largely because of the persistently high fecundity of female koalas living there. The urogenital strain of *Chlamydia* is not present on French Island, and it is for this reason the local koalas have maintained a rate of increase that is close to the maximum attainable by the species. How this came about and its implications are best understood by retelling the history of the population.

There were no koalas on 'Ile Francoise' in 1802 when it was circumnavigated and named by French explorers under the command of Nicholas Baudin. There is no evidence to suggest that koalas ever occurred there, despite the prevalence of coastal manna gum (*Eucalyptus prioriana*), one of their favourite food species. French Island, as it subsequently became known, remained koala-free until late in the nineteenth century when a small group of animals were deliberately released there by white settlers. The release site was somewhere on the north-east corner of the island and the founding group came from the nearby mainland.

The identity and motives of those who carried out this first introduction are obscure. The early accounts, by Fred Lewis and John McNally, suggest that the animals came from around Corinella, a small port on the mainland adjacent to French Island, and that they were moved to the island by either local farmers or fishermen. John McNally, the first wildlife scientist to study the French Island koala population, suggested that they were concerned about the animals' fate in the face of frequent bushfires on the mainland. French Island was thought to be a safe haven.

Oral history on French Island identifies only one man, Jim Peters, as being responsible for introducing koalas. Jim fits the general picture painted by McNally. He lived at Corinella and at various times was both a farmer and a seafaring man. He also seems to have been a very competent naturalist. He was introduced to native wildlife at an early age by his father, William Peters, who made a living from taxidermy. During their childhood, Jim and his five brothers and four sisters usually accompanied their father on his collecting trips to the nearby Bass Hills. Jim was obviously dutiful and during one trip he collected an unusual fairy possum that ended up being one of the type specimens of Victoria's only endemic mammal, Leadbeater's possum (*Gymnobelideus leadbeateri*).

The release of koalas onto French Island happened about thirty years later, around 1898, when Jim was an adult. Island lore has it that he gave a pair of young koalas as pets to a lady friend at Kiernan's Settlement, on the north-east corner of the Island, and that these animals subsequently escaped. However, this is an apocryphal story. It is equally likely that Jim had a nobler motive and acted to preserve a few koalas that had survived a recent bushfire. The fires of 1898 were the most severe for 50 years and razed almost all of Gippsland, including the forests of the Bass Hills. They would have undoubtedly devastated the area's koala population. A bushman with a naturalist's bent would have recognised the north-east corner of French Island as a safe refuge from fire as well as a place where manna gums were prolific. We will never know Jim Peters' motives, or whether he selected particular animals or simply relocated all he could find. The one thing we do know is that the animals he moved were free of *Chlamydia* and for this reason his relocation was extremely significant for the species in Victoria. (If nothing else, this demonstrates that in matters of conservation the individual can make a difference.)

Jim's koalas turned out to be a surprisingly fecund lot: they went forth and multiplied, very rapidly. With an area of 17 000 hectares, French Island is a big place, but within 25 years the progeny of this small group were seen all over the island. John McNally recorded that a local farmer counted 2300 koalas in a 8 kilometre stretch along the west coast in the early 1920s. About this time it became apparent that koalas were so abundant, and their demand for eucalypt foliage so great, that large areas of island's manna gum forests were being defoliated and killed (Plate 13). Local farmers were alarmed and even requested permission from the State Government to shoot the animals in order to save the trees. Their request was denied. Instead the government authorised a translocation program and offered the locals two shillings and sixpence per koala to catch, bag and deliver them to Tankerton jetty to be shipped to the mainland. Fifty koalas were shipped off to nearby Phillip Island in 1923. In the same year a group of six animals was sent to Kangaroo Island, in South Australia. A fauna

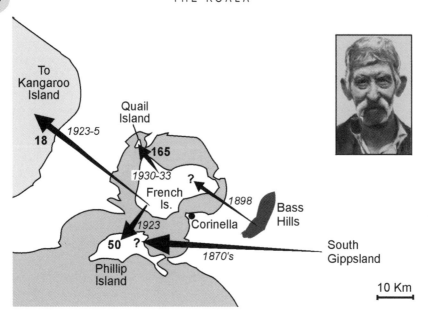

Figure 7.1
The early movements of koalas on and off the islands of Western Port, Victoria. The numbers of animals moved, where known, is shown in bold. Jim Peters (inset, from a newspaper photograph published in the late 1930s) is the man who probably started it all.

reserve had been recently established there under the patronage of Frederick Wood Jones, anatomist and Curator of Mammals at the Adelaide Museum. This was only a trial move but the animals fared well, and another 12 were sent to Kangaroo Island in 1925. (See Figure 7.1.)

Small numbers of koalas were captured on French Island each year after this and relocated to various destinations around Victoria. Between 1930 and 1933 a total of 165 were transferred to Quail Island, an island of just over 1000 hectares, tucked closely into shore at the northern end of Western Port. The subsequent history of this population is also worth retelling as it demonstrates in a most spectacular manner that the fecundity of Jim's koalas remained high, even when they were moved to another place.

THE QUAIL ISLAND CATASTROPHE

As a boy, Ronald Monro spent many happy days roaming around on Quail Island. It was uninhabited and surrounded by mud, mangroves and mosquitoes but it was still his 'treasure island'. In 1940 he went off to World War II and just before he embarked he made one last visit to his boyhood haunt. Over the years he had noticed that the population of koalas had been slowly increasing but on this visit he noted that 'The bears were everywhere'. In November 1943 he returned from the war and soon after revisited the island. What he saw moved him deeply and he wrote the following account, which appeared in one of Melbourne's major newspapers:

Last Sunday I visited [Quail] island for the first time since my return from overseas, and what I found almost made me weep. I was too angry to weep — I was stunned — but determined to do something, something to save the lives of at least some of the hundreds of starving koalas I found there.

Long before I got within a mile of the island I could see something was wrong. It was no longer a mass of greenery. The trees were bare and brown. As I got closer I could see that most of the trees were dead and the rest dying. I hurried across the narrow strip of marsh that separates the island from the mainland and there I found a scene of desolation, populated with emaciated bears.

Hundreds of starving bears, many with little babies clinging to their backs, were sitting up dead trees or slowly moving about in search of food. In some trees, where there were still a few stray leaves, bears were fighting for the meagre meal. Some bears were walking aimlessly about on the ground, too exhausted to climb any more in search of food.

With their thick woolly fur they still appear well and healthy from a distance, but all those I examined closely were just skin and bone, and the babies, were skinny weak little creatures.

Munro went on to suggest how the situation could be dealt with if the authorities acted immediately to 'organise a party of trained men to capture and crate the koalas and ship them to the mainland'. For several months the authorities procrastinated, insisting there was no problem, despite an on-going public castigation by some of the leading naturalists of the day (Figure 7.2). In early 1944 a film of the catastrophe was shown to the general public in a Melbourne theatre. This caused Mr Hyland, the then Chief Secretary of the Victorian Government, to issue a statement condemning the film as it 'conveyed the mistaken impression that the bears on the island were dying of starvation'. He went on to say that it was 'a common sight to see koalas sunning themselves on dead timber' but 'it was most unfortunate that the picture should be allowed to be distributed'. To avoid further embarrassment the government then used the powers of wartime censorship to prevent the film being shown outside Australia.

Eventually common sense prevailed and the suggestion made by Munro was acted upon. A translocation program was launched and over the following months a total of 1308 living koalas were captured and removed from Quail Island. Sixty dead animals were counted, but this was probably an underestimate. Overall, translocation was seen as an adequate solution to the problem and it has remained the standard method of dealing with over-abundance up to the present day. To date Victorian wildlife authorities have relocated over 14 000 koalas to more

than 200 release sites (Figure 7.3). The problem facing this program today is a looming shortage of suitable koala habitat, but this difficult management problem is discussed in the next chapter. It is important first to understand why over-population occurs in the first place.

FECUNDITY LEVELS AND THE RATE OF INCREASE OF *CHLAMYDIA*-FREE POPULATIONS

Fecundity essentially means productiveness, and the fecundity rate of a population is defined in terms of the number of young born per female per year. In Chapter 5 it was indicated that female koalas are physiologically capable of producing a single young per year. They can do this from the time they are sexually mature, at around 2 years of age, until they are 15 or more years old. This means that an average female is theoretically capable of producing up to 13 young in her life time. In a healthy ecosystem you would expect natural predators to account for many of these young, and for the population size to remain relatively stable. But with no natural predators, and an initially unlimited supply of food, it is a different story.

The eruption of the koala population on Quail Island was neither

Figure 7.2
This photograph of the koala population crash on Quail Island was published in September 1944 in the magazine *Wild Life*.

Figure 7.3
Total numbers of
koalas relocated
from the
Western Port
islands to other
parts of Victoria,
1923–1997.

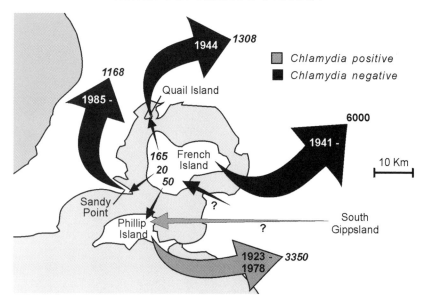

anticipated nor, for many years, understood. Despite their history of achieving very high population numbers in the 1890s, koalas were widely believed to be 'poor breeders'. The details of their biology simply were not known but it was widely believed that female koalas only produced a single young every second year. This 'fact' was repeated in the literature for many years, even after John McNally's research in the late 1950s had indicated that French Island koalas were capable of a high rate of reproduction and Ian Eberhard demonstrated in the 1970s that most female koalas on Kangaroo Island bred every year. It was not until the 1980s, when we monitored the reproductive performance of individuals over several years, that we came to understand how koalas were able to increase their numbers so rapidly.

For our study we selected a small population of koalas living in a coastal manna gum forest beside Red Bill Creek, near the north-western corner of French Island. We monitored this group for over three years and found that over this time almost all of the sexually mature females in the population gave birth to a single young each year. About 15 per cent of these young were lost during early pouch life (up to three months of age), but of those that survived pouch life almost 100 per cent survived to the time they became independent from their mothers. This data confirmed our impression that female koalas were very good mothers. But there were also no predators on French Island and subsequent to our study, Peter Mitchell showed that this high survival rate among young koalas persisted for the three years following their independence.

When we looked at the reproductive performance of female koalas

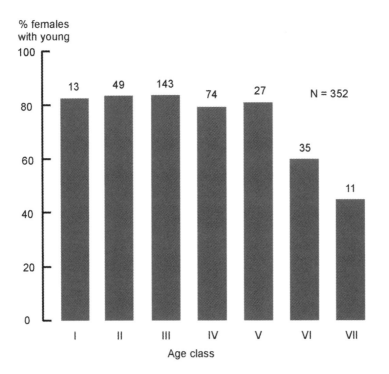

Figure 7.4
Fecundity rates
for different age
classes from a
sample of 352
females from the
Chlamydia-free
koala population
on French
Island, Victoria.

relative to their age, we found that the fecundity of the French Island females did not start to taper off until they were well over 10 years old. Adjudging age from the degree of tooth wear (see Figure 5.9, page 70), Wear Class V females (around 10 years old) were just as fecund as Class II females (2–3 years old). Our data showed that more than 80 per cent of animals up to and including Class V females successfully raised young each year. By the time females reached Class VI, which we estimated to be over 15 years old, fecundity had declined a little, but 60 per cent of females in this age class were still producing young each year. Combining all the age classes still gave a relatively high level of fecundity at the population level (approximately 80 per cent) and we began to realise the implications of this for population growth.

Population biologists have various ways of quantifying the growth rate of a population. One of the simplest is to express it as the percentage increase in the population per year. Another is the 'doubling time'; that is the number of years it takes a population to double its numbers. Estimates of doubling time are a valuable tool when making demographic projections and, over the years, population biologists have related various versions of the following story to illustrate this, as well as make the point that short doubling times, no matter how small a starting population, are potentially catastrophic. This is a 1990s version of the story:

Jobs are hard to get these days and young people have to be astute to earn a living. One young lady proposed a novel pay scheme to a prospective employer. She was inexperienced and in order to secure the job she offered to start work on a very low salary, one cent a day, provided the employer paid her each day and doubled her pay each succeeding day. The employer, a merchant banker, thought this sounded like a good deal and readily agreed. He was starting to have second thoughts by day 15 when his employee's daily pay was more than $160. He fled the country on day 25 when it had reached $167 772. Had he stuck around and kept to the original employment contract he would have paid out $5 368 709 for her thirtieth day on the job and a total salary of more than $10 million for the month.

When we reviewed our data on the French Island koala population we estimated that it was increasing at the rate of 28 per cent per year. We realised that if it maintained this rate the population had the potential to double its numbers in less than three years (see Figure 7.5). This appeared to be an extraordinary rate of increase. It meant that a koala population established with a very small founder group could increase to a very large number of animals in a relatively short time. For example, four koalas could increase to a population of around 1500 animals in just 25 years. Against the background of literature on koalas and of their perceived status as 'poor breeders' such a rate of increase seemed improbable. Even if it were theoretically possible you would expect most of the animals produced to either die or disperse away into the surrounding forest.

But on French Island there were no predators, and animals could not disperse off the island. This rate of increase would explain what

Figure 7.5
The potential growth rate of typical *Chlamydia*-free koala populations (solid line) compared to the *Chlamydia*-infected group (broken line). Each population was founded with 30 animals (15 males, 15 females). The shape of the growth curve is dependant on the level of fertility, which can differ widely between *Chlamydia*-infected populations (see Table 7.1). The growth curve for the *Chlamydia*-infected population displayed here is based on an overall fertility rate of 40 per cent.

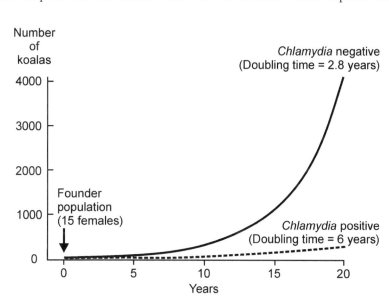

actually happened to the island's koala population between 1898 and the mid-1920s. It would similarly account for the events on Quail Island. The population founded there with 165 animals between 1930 and 1933 would have been approaching its fourth doubling in 1943. This would have resulted in a population approaching 3000 animals and account for the devastation observed by Ronald Monro. This estimate does not reconcile with the number that were finally removed but, given the politically charged nature of the Quail Island debacle, the estimate of the death toll could have been deliberately low.

By the 1980s the accounts of koala population crashes in the 1920s and 1940s were ancient history. It was not until we witnessed one ourselves that we became convinced that koalas were capable of achieving the high rates of increase that our population models suggested. This crash occurred in 1988 on Sandy Point, a small promontory jutting out from the western shoreline of Western Port, Victoria. Koalas were first introduced there in 1972, mainly into a 200-hectare patch of manna gum forest. The founding population was a group of 20 animals from French Island. This *Chlamydia*-free population grew rapidly. Over-browsing and tree-damage were apparent by the mid-1980s, and translocations by Victorian wildlife authorities to relieve this commenced soon after. However, the numbers removed were insufficient to stem the natural increase and when we visited the site in October 1988 the animals were literally falling out of the trees. The death and devastation were just as shocking for us as they had been for Ronald Monro on Quail Island 45 years earlier. There was a koala in almost every tree but barely any foliage left for them to eat. The animals were pathetically thin and many were obviously starving, stripping bark from the trees and eating it as a substitute for leaves. There were numerous dead animals on the ground and the bush stank from their rotting carcasses. We estimated a population of over 2000 in the 200-hectare plot of manna gum where the crash occurred, but only 1100 animals were eventually removed. Some animals dispersed but most of the rest died of starvation. Almost all of the manna gums on Sandy Point were killed.

The problem of koala over-population in Victoria remains unresolved today and several other koala populations have 'crashed' in recent years. These cases, and the management options available to deal with over-population, are discussed in the final chapter. The alternate case to consider, however, is the situation of populations where the natural rate of increase is slowed because of infertility in females.

CHLAMYDIA INFECTION, INFERTILITY AND ITS IMPACT ON KOALA POPULATIONS

Our own studies, and those of David Obendorf and others, have shown that permanent and irreversible infertility is one of the possible consequences for female koalas experiencing an infection with Type II (urogenital strain) *Chlamydia*. Also, as described in the previous chapter, not all females that are exposed to *Chlamydia* succumb to it, and the level of infertility varies greatly between infected populations (see Table 7.1, page 94).

In populations that have had no previous exposure to the urogenital strains of *Chlamydia*, the impact on the general level of fecundity is huge. Mortality rates, particularly as a result of cystitis, can also increase. The situation in the Grampians, where more than 95 per cent of the resident females were left permanently infertile after *Chlamydia* was inadvertently introduced, has already been described. With such low fertility the annual number of births in the population would be inadequate to replace the normal mortality from old age and other causes, much less the additional mortality caused by the *Chlamydia*-related disease (cystitis, for example). Such populations invariably decline. The koala population in the Grampians is now heading into a phase of low numbers from which it may take several decades to recover.

The impact of *Chlamydia* appears to depend on a number of factors, not all of which are understood. These factors include the strain of *Chlamydia* and the history of exposure of the population to it. The fecundity of the Grampians population is atypically low when compared to a number of other *Chlamydia*-infected populations from across the southern range of the koala (see Table 7.1). The fertility rate of 17 per cent we recorded on Phillip Island was also unusually low, and the reasons for this and its implications are discussed in the next section. In the majority of the *Chlamydia*-infected southern populations, fertility rates range between 35 and 55 per cent. Data collected by scientists Ben Weigler, Neil White and Noelene Kunst, during their work on koalas at Sheldon near Brisbane, suggest fertility levels of around 67 per cent in a *Chlamydia*-infected population there. In a long term study of an infected population near Oakey, in south-eastern Queensland, Greg Gordon and his colleagues from the Queensland National Parks and Wildlife Service, found fertility to vary over a 12 year period from a low of 27 per cent to a high of 55 per cent.

With normal levels of mortality, fertility rates above 35 per cent are considered adequate for a koala population to maintain its numbers. With this proportion of females breeding each year, the theoretical doubling time of the population is about ten years. When fertility rates slip below this however, or if mortality rates rise, the future viability of the population becomes doubtful. In their Oakey study Greg Gordon and his colleagues found that the koala population there declined steadily despite maintaining an average annual level of fertility of 41 per cent. They attributed this decline to increased mortality resulting from cystitis brought on by the chlamydial infection. In this case the population was experiencing a double whammy from the *Chlamydia*: depressed fertility and increased mortality.

Lower fertility rates result in relatively low rates of increase for a population and such a population can remain 'small' for a long time (see Figure 7.5). If mortality rates suddenly escalate during this time, even if only for a short period, such a population can quickly decline to extremely low numbers or even extinction. This balance between the levels of the fertility and mortality is the key to understanding the dynamics of koala populations, particularly small populations.

Table 7.1

Fertility rates (%) for some *Chlamydia*-infected koala populations, based on the number of independent females accompanied by dependent young.

Site	Females with young (%)	Source
Sheldon, south-east Qld.	67	White & Kunst 1991
Inverness (Oakey), south-east Qld.	mean: 41 range: 27–55	Gordon *et al.* 1991
South-east Qld.	67.5	Weigler *et al.* 1988
Grampians, Vic.	0	Martin & Handasyde 1991
Phillip Island, Vic.	17	Martin & Handasyde 1991
Stony Rises, Vic.	36	Martin & Handasyde 1991
Raymond Island, Vic.	40	Martin & Handasyde 1991
Brisbane Ranges, Vic.	45	Martin & Handasyde 1991
South Gippsland, Vic.	56	Martin & Handasyde 1991

SMALL POPULATIONS AND *CHLAMYDIA*

If a small koala population has a large area of good quality habitat into which to expand, and is lucky enough not to experience any natural catastrophes such as bushfires while it is still small, then relatively low fertility does not appear to prevent it eventually achieving a large population size. The history of the population on Phillip Island up to 1978 provides a good example of this (see below), and similar patterns can be seen in other populations established with *Chlamydia*-infected animals relocated from Phillip Island. Some of these populations have achieved such high numbers that they have become a management problem, the most worrisome at the present time being Snake Island, east of Wilson's Promontory, Victoria. Here a total of 133 koalas relocated from Phillip and French Islands in 1945 had increased to a population estimated to number 5000 in 1998. This population was causing severe defoliation to their food trees. (The management problems of Snake Island are discussed in the final chapter.)

Phillip Island and Port Macquarie, in northern New South Wales, are two of Australia's more famous destinations for tourists seeking koalas. Many Australians, and many overseas visitors, have had their first encounter with a free-living koala in one of these places. Both are small populations and both are infected with *Chlamydia*. Their histories illustrate the problems of populations facing both predicaments simultaneously.

The main process responsible for creating small populations, such as those found on Phillip Island and at Port Macquarie, is loss of habitat. This is ongoing and particularly acute on the fringes of Australia's major population centres along the eastern seaboard. There, urbanisation is the driving force leading to habitat loss (Figure 7.6), but large scale agricultural developments degrade huge areas of habitat in rural areas as well. Whatever their situation, habitat loss is the start of a syndrome of decline for many remnant koala populations. An elevation in mortality rate is one component of this syndrome, with motor cars and domestic dogs being the main koala killers in urban areas. Depressed fertility is often superimposed on this. When depressed fertility occurs together with small population size, the threat to the population is most serious and most difficult to address.

PHILLIP ISLAND

Phillip Island's koala population is not native. Koalas were first introduced there by local farmers, probably in a series of small releases starting from the 1870s. The founding animals came from a number of nearby locations, notably Gippsland and the Mornington Peninsula. It seems that some of these founders were infected with *Chlamydia* as the rate of increase of the Phillip Island population was initially slow and koalas remained in low abundance there for many years. However, by the 1940s they were so abundant that translocations to reduce numbers became necessary.

Figure 7.6
Urban
development
is a significant
cause of koala
habitat loss
in coastal areas.
Koala populations
living in such
areas are often
at risk.
(Kath Handasyde)

For many years this eruption of koalas on Phillip Island was attributed to the introduction of a group of 50 koalas from French Island in
1923. The growth rate of the population was thought to have acceler-
ated with introduction of these highly fecund French Island animals.
However, based on our current knowledge of the susceptibility of
naive animals to *Chlamydia*, we now think that this is unlikely to be
true. We believe that once these French Island animals came into
contact with *Chlamydia* they would have succumbed quickly, as they
have in the Grampians, and probably made little contribution to subsequent generations.

What is more likely is that the founder population of *Chlamydia*-
infected koalas on Phillip Island continued to breed, albeit with
depressed fertility resulting in a slow rate of population increase. The
population would have received set backs, particularly as a result of
bushfires, but over time koalas became abundant. From the records
kept during the translocations that took place during the 1940s, we
know that 40 per cent of the females were carrying young at this time.
If maintained, this level of fecundity would be sufficient for the population to double its numbers every seven years or so.

More than 3000 koalas were removed from Phillip Island during
the translocation program which began in 1941. When the program
was discontinued in 1978, three things were obvious. The first was
that over-browsed and defoliated trees, once common, were no longer
evident. The second was that the amount of prime koala habitat left

Figure 7.7
Much remnant
koala habitat
occurs along
roadsides and
many koalas are
run over and
killed by
passing cars.
(Kath Handasyde)

on the island had progressively shrunk to the point where less than 250 hectares remained. (Much of this habitat had been lost to residential and tourist developments.) The third point was that the fertility rate of the surviving koalas had declined markedly: in the last groups translocated, in 1977 and 1978, only 11 per cent of females had young.

By the mid-1980s the abundance of koalas on Phillip Island was so low that many were concerned that the population was headed for extinction. The low fertility rate was part of the reason for the decline but the immediate cause was the increasing number of koalas being killed. Some of this mortality was due to domestic dogs, but most occurred on the roads. The impact that this mortality was having on the population was not appreciated until the number of koalas had declined markedly. Over the years Phillip Island had become increasingly popular as a tourist destination and, somewhat ironically, the growing volume of tourist traffic using the island's roads appeared to be a factor in this rising koala mortality. As well, koalas were being increasingly drawn to the roads because a significant proportion of their remaining food trees now occurred by the roadsides (Figure 7.7). Depressed fertility and increased mortality continued throughout the 1980s, such that by 1988 the total population of koalas remaining on the island was estimated to be less than 100 animals.

There is no way of protecting wild koalas from *Chlamydia*, or of restoring the fertility of diseased animals, and so the initial approach adopted to reverse the decline on Phillip Island was to try to reduce mortality. Speed limits were lowered and signs erected to inform motorists of the extent of the koala road toll and encourage them to watch out for koalas on the roads. Koala road kills did decrease over the next few years but this probably reflected the very low number of animals now left on the island rather than the success of the program. By this time koalas were noticeably scarce and loud complaints were being heard from the tourist industry. As a response to this a reserve was established in one of the few remaining areas of intact habitat left on the island. A group of fertile females and a few adult males were introduced to this koala-proof enclosure and abundance allowed to increase naturally as the animals bred. Ten years later this semi-captive population is now the focus for tourists who come to Phillip Island seeking koalas. There are still free-ranging animals surviving and surplus koalas are being released from the reserve to supplement the wild population. In addition local community groups, such as the Friends of the Koalas, are planting koala food trees to extend the area of suitable habitat.

PORT MACQUARIE

A second example of a small population overcoming *Chlamydia* and other mortality problems is the recent history of the koalas at Port Macquarie, New South Wales. There are many similarities and some important differences between the Phillip Island and Port Macquarie koala populations. Above all, the history of the Port Macquarie koalas illustrates the significance of breeding success to the survival of small populations.

First settled in 1821, Port Macquarie was Australia's third convict settlement (after Sydney and Hobart). The first work that the convicts were put to was clearing the forest, and the little forest that remains today is regrowth. Koalas were endemic to the area and somehow survived this early clearing and became abundant by the turn of the twentieth century; so abundant that 'koala shoots' were not unusual around this time. In the 1930s, the remnant koala population experienced an epidemic of 'eye disease'. The population also survived this and now, with the help of local people, is enduring the second round of 'de-afforestation' that has come with the rapid urbanisation and tourist development in this area. To combat this the local community formed a Koala Protection Society, planted thousands of koala food trees and built a koala hospital to care for and, where possible, rehabilitate sick and injured animals for release back into the wild.

Motor cars and domestic dogs are the main cause of death and injury to koalas around Port Macquarie, as they are on Phillip Island. The impact of a high death rate on the two populations has been different, however, and this is largely because the populations differ in one crucial aspect: the fertility rate of the females. Over 50 per cent of females in the Port Macquarie population are still breeding, compared with less than 15 per cent on Phillip Island. This higher fecundity has so far enabled the Port Macquarie population to maintain its numbers despite the number of animals being killed each year. This and the continuous planting of food trees, are probably the main reasons why the population has persisted. In contrast, the low fecundity of the Phillip Island population is the primary reason why it is now hovering on the edge of extinction.

Wildlife populations often pass through phases of very low numbers, usually as a consequence of some natural disaster. Over millions of years of natural selection, however, species have acquired adequate reproductive potential to allow them to quickly recover their numbers following such a crash. (Those that did not simply aren't around any more.) This is why *Chlamydia* is such a significant disease for koalas, because it reduces fecundity rates and thus reduces the ability of a population to build up its numbers quickly. This is particularly threatening for small populations. To highlight the significance of 'smallness' the late Graeme Caughley, one of the most renowned wildlife scientists to work in Australia, once put it that the fate of a small population is governed by the specific fortunes of each of its few individuals. Applying this to a koala population comprised of only a small number of individuals, it can be seen how the loss of one or two breeding females can be very significant. While this is understood, we do not yet understand why the fertility rates of *Chlamydia*-infected populations differ so widely. This is reason for concern.

With the Phillip Island and Port Macquarie koalas, it seems that this difference in fertility rates is the key to their present status. We can only hypothesise about why this is so. It is possible that the two populations are infected with different strains of *Chlamydia* and one strain is more virulent than the other. It has been suggested that a concurrent infection with some other organism, a retrovirus for example, would influence susceptibility to *Chlamydia* but this remains to be demonstrated. It could also be because of differences in general health, as this too is known to influence disease susceptibility in animals. Stress has been widely touted as a key factor in this, but as yet there have been no studies that demonstrate such a relationship. The difference could even be due to nothing more than chance, and 'blind chance' often plays a role in the fate of small populations.

LOW ABUNDANCE POPULATIONS

Low abundance is characteristic of many koala populations throughout the range of the species. Low abundance populations are not necessarily small populations. They may be, but they can also be large populations, sparsely spread over a large area. In the extensive commercial forestry areas of northern New South Wales and south-east Queensland, for example, abundances of around one koala per 20–30 hectares appear to be typical, and this suggests a large and significant koala population in the area. Koalas occupying the semi-arid zone of central Queensland are even more sparsely distributed but, because of the size of the area, they are numerically a very large population. Other populations are numerically smaller but no less significant in their conservation value; the koalas occupying the forests of south-eastern New South Wales and far east Gippsland in Victoria being but two examples.

The habitat in Queensland's semi arid zone is very heterogeneous, with pockets of highly abundant populations in riverine habitats along the major watercourses, but much lower abundances elsewhere. Two biologists who have worked in this area, Alistair Meltzer and David Lamb, suggested abundances as low as one animal per 210 hectare away from the riverine sites. These scientists pointed out that there was over 200 000 square kilometres of semi-arid country suitable for koalas in central Queensland and this implies a koala population approaching 100 000 animals in this region.

The longer term studies of Greg Gordon reveal some of the biology of these arid-zone koalas, but largely because of their sparseness, they are more difficult to study than southern koalas. Based on morphological differences and some genetic data, Melzer and Lamb suggested that these koalas probably represent a distinct arid zone ecotype of the species and may even possess a range of behavioural and ecological adaptations for this environment. With their very short, silver-grey fur (presumably to reflect sunlight thereby reducing the chance of overheating) they certainly look very different to their southern cousins. It is truly remarkable, given the habitat, that a tree dwelling animal like a koala manages to survive in this region at all. Midsummer, midday temperatures regularly exceed 40°C, rainfall is irregular and drought frequent. While some areas are reasonably fertile, the productivity of the area generally is low. Coping with such conditions further underlines just how robust is the ecological strategy of this 'bear of little brain'.

The information available on the population biology of these arid-zone koalas comes from two sources. In the first of these Melzer and Lamb commented on there being only two juvenile animals and one female with a young in their small sample of 20 animals (14 females, 6 males) collected in brigalow scrub and mulga lands in central Queensland. This suggests extremely low fecundity but it is a very small sample. Greg Gordon's data from Springsure (in the same area) found much higher fecundity. At another semi-arid zone site further south, in the mulga scrubs and eucalypt woodlands of south-western Queensland, Gordon and his colleagues tested for *Chlamydia* and found no evidence of infection. Fertility at this site was initially very high, with 91 per cent of females breeding or lactating, but dropped back to 57 per cent in the face of a growing drought. This suggests that environmental conditions can have a substantial impact on fertility rates. Perhaps this is not surprising, given the very tight energy budget of the koala, even under benign environmental conditions. In the semi-arid zone the frequent droughts probably have an overriding influence on abundance. In the 1979–80 drought in this area an estimated 63 per cent of the koala population died in one year. Prolonged periods of sub-median rainfall and intense midsummer heat waves are common throughout these arid areas, and it is probable that they deliver regular checks to the growth rate of koala populations and therefore regulate their overall size.

The population biology of these arid zone animals appears to differ from those populations living in the more benign coastal environments. Over time, continuing field studies will further elucidate these differences. However, like the coastal populations, these animals from the dry country are seriously threatened by land clearing. Wildlife managers in these areas now face the nightmarish task of attempting to conserve these naturally sparse populations in remnants of habitat. This is the subject of the final chapter.

CHAPTER 8

CONSERVATION AND MANAGEMENT

This final chapter deals with some of the more pressing issues currently facing wild koala populations. These have collectively been termed as conservation and management issues, and while the meaning of the word 'conservation' is widely understood, the term 'management' is not. It is, in fact, the more general term, and in this sense embraces the full range of human involvement in manipulating wildlife populations.

Conservation is typically understood as action taken to protect or increase numbers in a wildlife population, and it is widely supported by the general public. However, when a species is causing economic damage or has simply become so abundant that it is degrading its own habitat, wildlife managers sometimes have to intervene to reduce numbers. This aspect of wildlife management is not as highly regarded by the general community, particularly when it targets a charismatic species.

We have striven throughout this book to emphasise that the koala has a very broad distribution, lives in a variety of habitat types and varies in abundance in different parts of its geographic range. A range of management problems confront different populations and different strategies must be adopted to address these. There is no universal approach. The complexities of koala management can be illustrated via a series of case histories, and a review of the current conservation status of the koala.

LEGAL STATUS

In order to discuss the management and conservation of koalas, it is important to establish who is legally responsible for them. The Australian Federal Government's jurisdiction is limited and largely restricted to matters of live exports and endangered species. Ownership of wildlife is vested in the Crown and it is therefore a state matter. Responsibility lies with the appropriate Minister of the Crown and in most Australian states this is the Minister for the Environment. These ministers exercise their responsibility subject to the laws passed by state parliaments.

It is important to point out that while a significant proportion of Australia's koala population today occurs on land that is privately owned — that is, land subject to freehold or leasehold title — this land title does not confer any proprietorial rights over the wildlife living on it. The wildlife remains the property of the Crown and koalas are a totally protected species in all states. The specifics of the legislation differ in each state but, without appropriate government permits, it is illegal to interfere with them in any way. The penalties are severe, particularly in Queensland where fines range up to $225 000 or two years imprisonment for illegally taking koalas from the wild.

Most wildlife biologists would quickly point out that protecting a species without protecting its habitat is a relatively useless gesture, and this is slowly being recognised by governments. In Victoria and Queensland, limited protection of habitat is achieved by vegetation clearance controls. More enlightened legislation exists in New South Wales in the form of a State Environment Planning Policy (SEPP 44). This obliges those who develop land to prepare plans of management for areas which contain 'core koala habitat'. What exactly constitutes core koala habitat remains problematic at the present time. Local governments in Queensland are required to 'consider' koala conservation in their planning schemes, and this is effective in areas where the local authority is sympathetic to conservation. The koala is such a significant species in the coastal areas south-east of Brisbane (now known as the 'Koala Coast') that a State Planning Policy (1/98) was specially enacted to protect habitat in this area.

ENDANGERED STATUS

Despite the widespread perception that the koala is a rare species, it does not meet any of the Australian Government's criteria for listing under its endangered species legislation as either an endangered or vulnerable species. Nor is it listed by the International Union for the

Conservation of Nature (IUCN). State wildlife agencies assign a conservation status to wildlife species within their borders and the status
of the koala in each is given in Table 8.1.

Table 8.1
The official status of the koala in each of the Australian states in
which wild populations occur.

State	Status	Relevant legislation
Queensland	Common wildlife	*Nature Conservation Act (1992)* *Nature Conservation Regulations (1994)*
New South Wales	Rare and vulnerable	*Threatened Species Conservation Act (1995)*
Victoria	Not designated. (See note below.)	*Wildlife Act (1975)*
Australian Capital Territory	Not designated	*Nature Conservation Act (1980)*
South Australia	Rare	*National Parks and Wildlife Act (1972)*

Note: In Victoria there is currently no legislation which formally lists the conservation status of wildlife species. However, the Atlas of Victorian Wildlife records the
distribution of all Victorian mammals, and a recent publication based on these
records (*Mammals of Victoria* 1995) described the koala as 'not threatened'.

As mentioned in the introduction to this chapter, an array of problems
confront different koala populations across the range of the species.
Generally, management initiatives to address these are confined to
local areas and conducted on a small scale. The first step in any such
initiative is to identify the problem and then devise an appropriate
strategy to deal with it.

HABITAT LOSS

Loss and degradation of habitat has already caused the extinction of
17 species of Australian mammals since European occupation and it
is still regarded as a threatening process for many species. The koala
is no exception.

HABITAT LOSS IN COASTAL AREAS DUE TO URBANISATION

Habitat loss is the most serious conservation issue for koalas in
coastal and adjacent hinterland areas of northern New South Wales
and south-eastern Queensland. Over the last few decades both

regions have experienced very high rates of growth in their human populations. Such growth had been good for business, and local economies have thrived, but it has been bad news for koalas (Plate 14). Koala habitat continues to be lost to both urbanisation and tourist development.

Koalas are more tolerant of habitat degradation than many other native species (they do not need an intact ground layer, for example, just intact trees) but the management problems become more acute with each additional hectare of bushland that is cleared. Some biologists also believe that habitat degradation renders koalas more susceptible to *Chlamydia* and hence leads to a rising level of infertility. Urbanisation is certainly accompanied by an elevation in the mortality rate and the Phillip Island scenario, of low fertility accompanied by high mortality, is a real possibility for some of these north coast populations. So far, infertility does not seem to be having a large influence in the north, but the epidemiology of *Chlamydia* in wild koalas is still poorly understood and we cannot be confident that it will not play a role in the future. As discussed in Chapter 7, *Chlamydia* is particularly threatening for small populations and many of these northern populations are small. If the fertility rate in any of these populations collapses then they will decline and possibly disappear within a decade or so.

Local governments have significant control over land use in these coastal areas, and some initiatives have already been taken to protect koala habitat. These include planning controls, revegetation programs (including plantations of preferred food species linking habitat remnants), community education, and legislation directed at traffic and dog control. Local governments, however, have to strike a balance between competing interests. The section of the community that is interested in koala conservation needs to be vigilant and keep themselves informed about local land use decisions and the status of the local koala population.

LAND CLEARING FOR AGRICULTURE IN AREAS OF LOW POPULATION ABUNDANCE

Habitat loss due to large scale land clearing for agricultural and pastoral development is the most serious threat facing the koala populations of the semi-arid woodlands of central and south-western Queensland. Information from GIS satellite imagery indicates that around 500 000 hectares of this woodland is being cleared annually. The koala is a rare species throughout this area and because its abundance is so low, monitoring is difficult and it is hard to discern population trends or put a figure on the impact of the clearing on the koala populations. This is a significant problem for wildlife managers and koala researchers alike.

These semi-arid woodlands are very sensitive ecosystems and it is ecologically irresponsible — and even over the medium term almost certainly not economically worthwhile — to clear them. The history of many civilisations, in the Americas, Africa and the Middle East, suggests that the ultimate result of tampering with dry lands is the creation of desert. Yet we are clearing them and this is a very difficult problem to address. For many, particularly people living in these semi-arid areas who make an income from such enterprises, the land is an inexhaustible resource. Not to clear and not to 'improve the land' is viewed as a missed opportunity.

To make wildlife conservation even more difficult, this clearing is done with the tacit support of government. Much of this land is leasehold and the Queensland Government has the power to dictate the terms under which it is used. If they were to ban or restrict clearing within 50 metres of watercourses, much valuable habitat would be preserved and the future of the koala populations ensured. However, the government fears that any attempt to impose clearing controls would be deeply resented by the rural community, and lead to the government's rapid exit from the treasury benches should they be foolhardy enough to try.

Community education and government policies that encourage a more realistic evaluation of these projects, and factor in the longer-term environmental costs, seem to be the only management initiative that can be taken. An enlightened society would see this dry land clearing for the folly that it truly is, but it takes time to shift viewpoints, particularly in conservative regions of the country. Significant amounts of habitat have already been lost and the rates of clearing are very high. There is not a great deal of time to preserve what remains. Protection of vegetation along water courses and drainage lines should be given the highest conservation priority.

CLEAR-FELLING OF NATIVE FOREST FOR WOOD PRODUCTS

Land clearing is also an issue in the wetter forests further south, particularly in south-eastern New South Wales, where large tracts of eucalypt forest are being clear-felled for timber production (much of it destined for wood pulp). The koala is listed as a rare and vulnerable species in New South Wales and the impact that timber harvesting is having on these southern populations is uncertain. Koalas are sparsely distributed in this region and the few that remain are now the only representatives of a large population that once occurred here. The conservation of these remnant populations has been the focus of a long-running battle over clear-felling in this area and in recent years a number of parks and reserves have been created. These may suffice and the koalas in this area may now be secure. However, conservation groups need to continue to press governments to adopt policies that encourage a more realistic evaluation of these projects. These forests are community assets and the community must decide whether cutting them down to produce relatively low value products, such as wood pulp, is more desirable that setting them aside for their intrinsic values, which include the conservation of wildlife.

BUSHFIRE

Bushfire has always been a factor in the viability and persistence of koala populations, particularly in the eucalypt forests of south-eastern Australia which are widely recognised as being among the most fire-prone regions on earth. Bushfires can be a threatening process, but this largely depends on their intensity and scale. While low-intensity, patchy fires kill individual koalas, they may not have a significant impact on the population. High-intensity fires on the other hand have the potential to eliminate koalas from wide tracts of forest and are thought to be one of the main causes for the demise of koala populations over large areas of Victoria in the early days of white settlement (as discussed in Chapter 2).

As well as eliminating koala populations, intense bushfires also destroy their habitat. However, over their long history the eucalypt forests of the south-east have adapted to recover from fire surprisingly quickly. The time necessary for them to recover to the point where they once again provide suitable habitat for koalas depends on a number of factors. These include the composition of the forest, the seasonal conditions subsequent to the fire and, most importantly, the patchiness and intensity of the original fire. Koalas may naturally recolonise a forest, but if they do not then the appropriate management strategy is to reintroduce them. A recent study in New South Wales indicates that this can be done a surprisingly short time after a fire.

A few weeks subsequent to the 1993 fires in the Port Stephens area of northern New South Wales, Steve Wykes from the National Parks and Wildlife Service successfully reintroduced koalas to a burnt out area. He found that the new growth that coppiced out from the trunks and branches of the blackened trees shortly after the fire provided plenty of food for them. While the results of this study were fascinating, they were not all together surprising — considering the long period of association between koalas and the fire-prone eucalypt forests of eastern Australia.

DISEASE

The threat that disease holds for koala populations has been extensively discussed in Chapter 6. Disease, particularly that caused by infection with *Chlamydia*, poses the greatest threat to small populations.

Continuing research into the virulence and pathogenicity of the various strains of *Chlamydia* will enable management strategies to be further refined. At present, the most appropriate strategies to address this problem are the close monitoring of vulnerable populations and the protection of breeding females.

OVER-POPULATION

The final management issue is the horrendous problem of over-population. In the southern part of their geographic range, in Victoria and South Australia, the containment of burgeoning koala populations occupying patches of remnant habitat is the most pressing problem now facing wildlife managers. Because it is such a complex and controversial issue it needs to be dealt with it at some length.

It was the Reverend Thomas Malthus who first observed that populations tend to rise faster than their food supply. Malthus made his observation in 1803 and he was talking about our species, *Homo sapiens*. He went on to suggest that struggle and starvation are an inevitable result of food shortage. This line of thought was apparently seminal for Charles Darwin when he put together his theory of natural selection later in the same century. Modern day ecologists continue to see the relevance of Malthusian thought to animal populations, particularly in situations where natural predators have been removed from the system.

Several so-called 'green revolutions' have enabled our species, *Homo sapiens*, to bring about quantum leaps in food supply and, for the present at least, defy Malthus and keep food supply abreast of population growth. However, there are unlikely to be any green revolutions for koalas. The foliage of eucalypts will remain their staple diet and eucalypt trees will take as long to grow as they always have. As a consequence, the management of koala populations in small isolated patches of habitat will remain a very difficult problem.

The management problems of over-population can be illustrated by examining case histories of over-abundance in two koala populations, each in a different wildlife jurisdiction. These are Framlingham, in Victoria, and Kangaroo Island, in South Australia.

THE FRAMLINGHAM STORY

Framlingham is a 1200-hectare isolate of native forest bordering the Hopkins River in western Victoria. It was an Aboriginal mission site in colonial times and retains its name from then. It is now owned by descendants of the original indigenous inhabitants, the Girai Wurrung people.

Framlingham is one of the few remnants of native forest left in this area. On the higher ground this forest consists of mixed stringybark (*Eucalyptus obliqua*) and peppermint (*E. radiata*) woodlands, with stands of swamp gum (*E. ovata*) and manna gum (*E. viminalis*) growing on the wetter and better quality sites. The latter two are highly preferred food species for Victorian koalas. There were almost pure stands of manna gum on the slopes going down to the river, with river red gums (*E. camaldulensis*) growing along the banks.

A koala population was established at Framlingham in the early summer of 1970 with 37 animals translocated from French Island. Conditions were excellent for koalas at Framlingham and the population appears to have expanded quickly. Assuming a doubling time of 2.8 years (a relatively conservative rate of increase for a *Chlamydia*-free koala population in Victoria) such a founding group would have multiplied to a population of about 5500 animals by 1990. Around this time local people noticed that koalas suddenly seemed very abundant and they started to become concerned about the impact that so many animals might have on the trees. They had good reason to be concerned

By 1993, after one more doubling, the population would have exceeded 10 000 animals (see Figure 8.1) and at this abundance there would almost be an animal in every second tree. According to local people, it was like that. Naturalists and farmers from the surrounding area became seriously alarmed and started to lobby the wildlife authorities to do something. Nothing was done and, by the summer of 1994/95, many of the trees were dead and the koalas too were starting to die. This disgraceful situation continued on for several more summers.

Figure 8.1
The eruption and crash of the koala population of Framlingham, Victoria, established with 37 animals in 1970. The background scene is of koalas and their young sitting in the trees they have defoliated.

Each year more trees died and more koalas starved. Animals dispersed onto surrounding farmland and, as their numbers grew, they began defoliating the old manna gums scattered through these areas. In the absence of any guidance from wildlife authorities, local farmers took their own initiatives to save these trees. Some put sheet metal bands around their bases to keep the koalas from climbing them, others resorted to shooting the animals. Today, the trees on these farms are the only mature manna gums surviving in the Framlingham area.

By the summer of 1998 almost all of the manna gums growing beside the Hopkins River were either dead or very close to it (Plate 15). They had previously covered an area well in excess of 200 hectares. Wildlife authorities eventually began translocating animals in April 1998 and continued this on through the winter. By August, when the program was discontinued, they had removed just over 1000 animals.

As pointed out at the beginning of this chapter, ownership of wild koalas is vested in the Crown and their welfare and management is the responsibility of the appropriate government minister. Over-abundant koala populations are a very difficult problem for politicians to deal with, and they generally deal with them badly. This was the case in 1943 when the Victorian Chief Secretary withstood four months of hectoring from prominent naturalists before he acted on what was obviously a crisis situation on Quail Island (see Chapter 7). All the time he was obfuscating, koalas were starving and by the time translocations began, in early 1944, some hundreds of animals had died. Over the years Victoria has seen a number of repeats of the Quail Island fiasco: Sandy Point in 1988/89 was one (Plate 16), Snake Island in 1997/8 another. Framlingham is the most recent and it appears that nothing has been learned in the 55 years since the Quail Island crash. At Framlingham wildlife authorities procrastinated for four years rather than four months. Over this time many thousands of koalas undoubtedly starved to death and hundreds of hectares of remnant eucalypt forest were degraded or destroyed. The cruelest irony of all is that the Framlingham crash happened on Aboriginal land. The erstwhile hunters of the koala had to stand by and watch them starve to death, powerless to do anything about it.

While recognising that there is little vacant habitat left for koalas in Victoria, wildlife authorities there continue to manage over-abundance by translocation. Recently, however, they have introduced a few refinements. When the surviving koalas at Framlingham were eventually translocated, adult males were sterilised by vasectomy. This is a surgical procedure whereby the seminal ducts (the vas deferens) are severed while the testes, which produce semen as well as the male hormone testosterone, are left intact. Vasectomised males act and mate normally but the matings are sterile and no offspring are produced. No sterilisation procedures were carried out on the females translocated from Framlingham nor on their pouch-young and, under these circumstances, the efficacy of sterilising the adult males seems dubious. It would lower the reproductive rate of the translocated females for a season or two but they would start breeding again when the male pouch-young translocated with them reached sexual maturity.

Kangaroo Island, South Australia

A similar problem of over-abundance was recently dealt with by wildlife authorities in South Australia and it is illuminating to review the approach they adopted. Before doing so, a brief history of koalas in South Australia, and of the Kangaroo Island population in particular, will set the scene.

The historic distribution of koalas in South Australia is not accurately known but they are believed to have been restricted to the forests of the south-eastern corner of the state. The last wild koala seen in South Australia, in the early 1930s, was in this area. This endemic population is believed to have gone to extinction sometime late in that decade. For some years prior to that, field naturalists in South Australia were becoming increasing concerned about the deteriorating status of the state's indigenous fauna. In 1918 a large reserve, subsequently to be known as Flinders Chase National Park, was established on the western end of Kangaroo Island to preserve native fauna. In December 1923, six koalas from French Island were released into a wire enclosure there. In April 1925, a further 12 French Island animals were added to the original group. Some of these animals escaped and, as the condition of the enclosure deteriorated, all of the captives were eventually set free. As with French Island koalas released in other places, they multiplied rapidly. By 1948 koalas were reported to be 'present in hundreds' around Flinders Chase.

While there is still more than 200 000 hectares of native vegetation left on Kangaroo Island, only a small amount of this is suitable for koalas. The most highly preferred habitat occurs along the river valleys and totals less than 1500 hectares. Severely defoliated and dying trees were first officially reported around Flinders Chase in the mid 1960s but tree damage had probably been evident for some years before this. In the 1950s small groups of Flinders Chase koalas were relocated to other parts of Kangaroo Island, notably the valley of the Cygnet River. Further translocations took place in the 1960s, mostly to other parts of the island and a few to the mainland, but the practice was discontinued after this. Subsequent to this, there was no official management of the population. Our experience with similar populations in Victoria tells us that it must have been expanding rapidly. Curiously, no population crashes were reported in the 1970s and 1980s. So what was controlling the koala population over this time? It is a sensitive subject, but hearsay suggests that regular culling was adopted by local people as an expedient and humane method of dealing with the problem.

Over-abundance continued to be a problem on Kangaroo Island and in April 1996 the State Minister for the Environment set up a Koala Management Task Force. The Task Force included representatives from scientific, conservation and animal welfare groups as well as from state and local government agencies. In their final report, delivered in late 1996, the task force listed and discussed each of the options available for dealing with the habitat degradation being caused by the over-abundant koala population on Kangaroo Island. Seven possible management strategies were reviewed. These were:

- Do nothing.
- Protect and restore the degraded habitat.
- Suppress fertility by introducing the urogenital strain of *Chlamydia*.
- Suppress fertility by either surgical or hormonal means.
- Translocate surplus animals to other sites.
- Transfer surplus animals to zoos and wildlife parks.
- Cull surplus animals.

These seven options, plus the additional one of removing the entire population, have repeatedly been suggested as methods of dealing with the problem of over-population in koalas. No one of them is a complete solution, but they are useful as a framework to discuss the problem.

MANAGEMENT OPTIONS

Do nothing
The 'do nothing' option is seen by many as the 'natural method' of population regulation in koalas. Framlingham is a good illustration of the outcome if such a policy is adopted. Without intervention, large areas of forest are killed and large numbers of koalas starve to death. Eventually the koala population, the forest and the other wildlife species that depend on it are all lost. It is cruel and stupid to allow this to happen. As a 'management strategy' it does not warrant further discussion.

Protecting degraded habitat
Implementing the second strategy, protecting and eventually restoring habitat, addresses the effect of over-population but not the problem

itself. Fencing koalas out of areas where the trees are badly defoliated is simply excluding the animals from their most preferred habitat and denying them access to their preferred food. It gives the trees respite and time to recover and from that point of view it is superior to the first option. But, in effect, it is still regulating population size by restricting food supply. Ultimately it will lead to malnutrition and the eventual death by starvation of many koalas, and this is no more humane than the first option.

Habitat protection and restoration do have a role, but only after the problem of koala over-population is first addressed. These options also require a great deal of time and large budgets to implement. Fences can be erected to protect habitat but koalas can climb almost anything and koala-proof fences are expensive. So is protecting individual trees with tree guards. For example, consider Framlingham where there are tens of thousands of trees spread across 1200 hectares. It would have been very difficult and very expensive to place guards on them all. But then it will also take 50 to 100 years, and a great deal of effort, to re-establish the manna gum forest that has been killed.

REMOVE THE ENTIRE POPULATION

It has often been suggested that the best and most cost-effective way to deal with the 'feral' populations of koalas on off-shore islands is to totally remove them. It would deal with the problem in one go and remove the need for on-going (and expensive) intervention by state wildlife authorities.

Such was the intention of John McNally, one of the first wildlife scientists to be confronted by the problem, when he first went to French Island in the mid-1950s. McNally was employed by the Victorian Government and his instructions were to remove all of the koalas from the Island. He told the French Islanders of his mission and they were highly amused. In fact, they were still telling the story 30 years later when we first went there to study koalas. One elderly farmer told us that it had been suggested to McNally at the time that he buy a house on the island because he would probably be there for the rest of his life. By the 1950s the locals had been dealing with the 'koala problem' for decades and they had some appreciation of just how many koalas there were and of how rapidly a few could multiply into many. McNally and his team did spend several months on the island and removed several hundred koalas but, as subsequent translocation records indicate, there were still plenty left when they went home.

People who seriously put forward total removal as a solution do not appreciate the scale of the problem. French Island is over 17 000 hectares in area, Kangaroo Island with over 200, 000 hectares of native vegetation alone, is considerably larger. While koalas are most abundant in their optimal habitat, usually manna gum woodlands, they also occur, albeit at low abundance, in most other habitats. Both islands are covered by large areas of sub-optimal habitat, heathlands in the case of French Island and mallee woodlands on Kangaroo Island. Koalas are scattered throughout both habitats and anyone who has spent time searching for them there will appreciate just how elusive they can be. After you have spent a week or so pushing your way through dense vegetation, your original optimism, that you are going to find all the koalas in a particular area, evaporates. In such large areas it is simply impossible. And, as the history of French Island subsequent to John McNally's visit shows, you do not have to overlook too many koalas for them to recolonise optimal habitat and once again breed up to large numbers.

SUPPRESS FERTILITY WITH *CHLAMYDIA*

Chlamydia is widespread in mainland koala populations and suppresses their fecundity (see Chapters 6 and 7). For this reason some have suggested that it is 'the natural regulator of koala populations' and should be introduced to control over-population. There are several objections to this. The first, and greatest, is an ethical one. Given the ethical constraints that all scientists and wildlife managers now work under, the question that must be asked is whether it is acceptable to deliberately introduce disease, particularly a disease of the reproductive tract, to a naive population of koalas. Having never been exposed to *Chlamydia*, they have no natural immunity to it and would be very susceptible. An ascending infection of the reproductive tract is, as any human female who has had pelvic inflammatory disease will testify, a lingering and painful condition. It would be a very cruel thing to do.

Another objection to this strategy is that, when it comes to koalas, there may be nothing 'natural' about *Chlamydia*. As discussed in Chapter 6, there is accumulating evidence that at least some of the strains of *Chlamydia* that infect koalas are not endemic and may been have transferred from domestic animals. Using *Chlamydia* to regulate the abundance of naive koala populations is really not an option. The suggestion is abhorrent to animal welfare groups, the general public and most wildlife scientists, and it is unlikely to ever receive ethical approval.

Ethical considerations aside, it would also be a very risky strategy. It is known from the history of the Grampians (Chapter 6) that *Chlamydia* will cause widespread infertility in a naive population, leave over 99 per cent of females infertile, and drive the population into a phase of very low numbers that will persist for decades. Should some other catastrophe, such as a large bushfire, befall the population during this time it may well be wiped out. The management objective with most of these island populations is to reduce their size and rate of growth: not eliminate them entirely.

The final point to be made here is that over-population is also a problem in many populations that are already infected with *Chlamydia*. Such was the case on Phillip Island prior to 1978, and it is the case now on Snake Island and the Strathbogie Plateau.

SUPPRESS FERTILITY BY SURGICAL OR HORMONAL INTERVENTION

Suppressing fertility by sterilising animals has now been tested in both South Australian and Victorian koala populations. Both surgical and chemical techniques have been used and all seem to have been reasonably successful. The main shortcoming of these techniques is their cost. Catching, anaesthetising and carrying out surgical procedures on koalas is relatively expensive. For the surgery alone it costs between $45 and $70 to vasectomise each male, and double that for a tubal ligation of a female. In 1997/98 more than $650 000 was spent on catching, sterilising and relocating 2500 animals on Kangaroo Island. Over the same time more than $300 000 was spent on similar management operations in Victoria. This was largely funded by taxpayers, and one has to question whether this is a reasonable use of the scarce resources now available for conservation programs. Even if we restrict ourselves to koala conservation, this sort of money could be spent much more effectively. Habitat preservation, for example, is widely acknowledged as the most cost-effective form of conservation. How many hectares of habitat could be bought and set aside with the $1 million that has so far been spent on these management exercises?

Chemical methods of sterilisation, particularly hormonal implants in females, may be more promising. They will be cost-effective if the animal does not have to be captured first for the implant to be put in place. Darting animals with implants has been used to regulate fertility in other wildlife populations and a similar technique has potential for koalas. However, even with efficient methods of delivery, hormonal implants are only useful for small and relatively accessible populations, that is, populations comprising no more than a thousand or so animals and these living in areas where the canopy height is less than 20 metres. Implanting and monitoring larger populations of koalas would be impractical. Small populations would still require intense monitoring to ensure that at least 70 per cent of the adult females are implanted and infertile each year. On-going programs of this nature would be expensive and wildlife authorities have far higher priorities than to spend large amounts of money on the management of such a common species.

Fertility control also suffers from the disadvantage that it does not reduce the population size, just the growth rate. In many cases koala populations are already too large when the problem of over-population is first perceived or acted upon. In these cases the population density must first be reduced to the carrying capacity of the habitat before fertility controls can be applied. This leaves the problem of what to do with the surplus animals. There are really only two options: translocate them or kill them.

TRANSLOCATION

Koalas have been translocated around Victoria since 1923, with a more or less formalised program existing since the translocation of large groups of animals began in 1944. The program had two main objectives. The first was to reduce abundances at over-populated sites, the second to reintroduce koalas to parts of their former range from which they were thought to have disappeared since European occupation. With the latter objective the program has worked very well in so far as koalas are now widespread in Victoria. As a method of controlling over-abundance, however, translocation has proved to be a short-term solution. Thousands of koalas have now been translocated over the last 50 years, particularly from French Island (see Figure 7.3, page 89), and over-abundance, tree defoliation and tree death are still a significant problem there. As well, poor selection of release sites, especially releasing animals into isolates of habitat such as at Framlingham, have achieved little more than transfer the problem elsewhere, albeit with a 15 to 20-year time lag before over-population again becomes a problem.

To circumvent this occurring in South Australia, all the animals recently translocated from Kangaroo Island were first surgically sterilised. Limited sterilisations have also been undertaken in some of the most recent translocations in Victoria and, as there is now a growing shortage of suitable release sites in that state, sterilisation is likely to become a standard procedure in that program as well.

Within the Victorian program there is also the growing realisation that the widespread translocation of what is a relatively inbred strain of koalas from French Island may have had an impact on the genome of the state's koala population as a whole. Genetic studies by Bronwyn Houlden, Bill Sherwin and colleagues from the University of New South Wales have shown that the level of genetic heterogeneity in Victorian and South Australian koala populations is significantly lower than that found in koala populations in Queensland and New South Wales. This was to be expected, given the management history of these populations. The lowest level of heterogeneity found by Houlden and Sherwin was on Kangaroo Island. The next lowest was in the source population itself, on French Island, and, as recounted in Chapter 7, the history of this population suggests that it was also established with a very small group of animals. Studies of the DNA from cell mitochondria, by Andrea Taylor from Macquarie University, support this. Mitochondria are organelles that live inside the cell and their DNA is derived from the mother only. Based on her study of mitochondrial DNA from French Island koalas, Andrea's data indicated that the population may have been established with as few as two females. The upshot of this research is that koalas from French and Kangaroo Islands may not be the best quality stock for re-establishing koala populations in Australia, even if there was suitable habitat left to contain them.

The final point worth making about the efficacy of translocations is the cost. Depending on the distance they are transported, catching and translocating koalas costs between $100 and $200 per animal. This is perhaps not a great deal of money per individual animal, but when we consider the total number of koalas at the many sites in Victoria currently experiencing over-population problems, it becomes a very large sum indeed. This is particularly pertinent given the unpromising genetic background of most of these animals. To continue spending large sums of money on them is simply wasting scarce conservation dollars on a species which is not endangered or even vulnerable. This brings us to the last and most difficult option: this is to harvest and utilise surplus animals or simply to kill them.

CULL SURPLUS ANIMALS

The Koala Management Task Force that was set up by the South Australian Minister for the Environment in April 1996 to address the problems of over-population on Kangaroo Island consisted of 11 members. They represented a wide range of viewpoints and included professional zoologists, wildlife managers, farmers and land holders as well as representatives of animal welfare organisations and local authorities. They were unanimous in their recommendations, the first of which was that: 'koala numbers at severely affected sites on Kangaroo Island be reduced immediately through a culling program.' The task force considered culling to be 'effective and applicable in the short term' and 'the only humane and realistic method of achieving an initial reduction in koala numbers to an ecologically sustainable level'. It would certainly be more humane than allowing the animals to starve to death.

This recommendation received a great deal of local and international media coverage. The response of the public, particularly from the international audience, was overwhelmingly negative. A tourist boycott and even trade sanctions were threatened. This was surprising, and a little hypocritical, as culling is widely used to control

wildlife populations in most overseas countries (including the United States). Understandably, the South Australian Government did not pursue this option (and the minister's predicament is illustrated in Figure 8.2) but decided on a program that included sterilisations, translocations, habitat protection and revegetation, management-orientated research, and community education. The merits of all but one of these have been canvassed above, and this last is perhaps the most important: this is community education.

COMMUNITY EDUCATION

As part of this public education campaign, the South Australian National Parks and Wildlife Service developed a Teacher and Student Information and Activity Pack that was distributed to schools. It set out all of the options and gave the reasons for the course eventually taken by the government. In discussing culling it said that it 'is a recognised wildlife management technique for the control of animals where their numbers exceed the carrying capacity of the habitat or cause damage to stock, crops or property'. It went on to point out that the government regularly issued destruction permits for other wildlife species including kangaroos, emus, hairy-nosed wombats, tammar wallabies, brush-tailed possums and Adelaide rosellas. It further

Figure 8.2
Peter Nicholson's cartoon, which first appeared in *The Australian* newspaper, is an incisive summary of the koala situation on Kangaroo Island in late 1996.

pointed out that in the view of most scientists and land managers the best option for Kangaroo Island was to use culling to achieve the initial reduction in koala numbers to an ecologically sustainable level followed by fertility control to maintain this level. This remains the view of most wildlife scientists and land managers who have an intimate knowledge of the problem.

MANAGEMENT OF OVER-ABUNDANCE IN THE FUTURE

Prior to, and during the public debate about the options for dealing with Kangaroo Island's surplus koalas, several other koala populations, from Victoria, were experiencing over-population problems. They received little or no publicity at the time but, taken together, a total of more than 10 000 koalas were involved. Some initiatives were taken to manage these populations but, given the number of animals involved, the programs were not adequately resourced and little more than a token effort: a case of 'too little, too late'. At Snake Island in Corner Inlet in southern Victoria thousands of mature manna gums were killed and an undetermined number of koalas died. At Framlingham in western Victoria thousands of koalas starved to death and hundreds of hectares of manna gum forest were killed. At Sandy Point, on Western Port, large areas of forest were already dead and the koala population there almost defunct. At the time of writing a similar disaster confronts a koala population estimated to number 15 000 animals at Mount Eccles in western Victoria. It is not going to end with these. Within a decade or so we will be facing more population crashes, some of them on a much large scale than the ones we have already seen. One of the larger ones will be on the Strathbogie Plateau in north-eastern Victorian.

LARGE SCALE OVER-POPULATION: THE STRATHBOGIE RANGES, VICTORIA

The history of koalas in the Strathbogies reflects, in a microcosm, the history of koalas in Victoria. When the area was first occupied by European settlers, between 1845 and 1870, koalas were present but in low abundance. With the demise of the indigenous hunters, koala abundances increased and for a time they were quite abundant. By the early decades of the twentieth century, however, they appear to have died out, presumably from the combined impact of that 'baneful quartet': land clearing, pelt shooting, bushfire and disease. Over the last decade we have asked many old people in the Strathbogies if they could remember seeing koalas when they were children. None could. The first koalas they could remember were the ones the wildlife department released there, beside Spring Creek on the outskirts of the township of Strathbogie, in the early years of World War II.

These first 30 animals came from Phillip Island, as did most of the 350 koalas that were subsequently released in various places on the plateau between 1941 and 1945. There is over 50, 000 hectares of eucalypt forest on the plateau and this relatively small group of founders just melted into it. One old man who witnessed the release told us that he seldom saw a koala for many years after that. When he did it was usually in a roadside tree and he would always rush home and pack the family into the car and drive back to the place so they could all see it — it was such a special thing to see a koala. Over the years he saw more and more koalas by the road and eventually it was not such a special thing any more. 'Now' he said 'they're everywhere.'

Their abundance was confirmed in 1994 when Sharon Downes from the University of Melbourne examined the use of the roadside corridors by native mammals in the Strathbogies. She compared their abundance and diversity in remnant forest with roadside corridors that were either close by or distant from patches of remnant forest. She surveyed six separate sites for each of these habitat types (a total of 18 sites) and found koalas to be uniformly abundant with an average of more than eight animals per hectare across sites. In subsequent surveys we have found koala abundances to vary with forest type. The habitat in which Sharon worked is dominated by manna gum (*Eucalyptus viminalis*) and blue gum (*E. globulus*). It is the richest habitat in the Strathbogies for arboreal species and has the highest abundance of koalas. The poorest habitat is on the drier hillsides and broad-leafed peppermint (*E. dives*) is the dominant species there. However, even in this habitat, there is around one koala per hectare.

The koalas in the Strathbogies, being derived from Phillip Island founders, are *Chlamydia*-infected and the fertility of the females is somewhat depressed. However, about 40 per cent are breeding and such a population has the potential to increase its numbers by about 10 per cent a year and double in size every five to seven years (see Figure 7.5, page 91). There have been no catastrophic bushfires between 1941 and 1998 to significantly interfere with the steady growth of the population. (The 1991 fire, the largest in recent years, was mainly confined to farmland on the western side of the plateau. The large blocks of forest on the eastern side were untouched.) Modelling the growth of this founder group of 350 animals with a doubling time of six years would suggest a notional koala population in excess of 200 000 animals now exists on the plateau. With 50, 000 hectares of forest and population abundances of between one and eight animals to the hectare, there may well be a population that large.

However, the absolute number is not important. What is important is that the koala population of the Strathbogies has slowly increased over the last 50 years to the point where it is now a very large population. As many of the females are still breeding, we believe it is still increasing. From what we have seen in other koala populations in Victoria, we have every reason to believe that the Strathbogie population will keep increasing until, as Malthus postulated, it reaches the limits of food supply. Then their food trees will die, the koalas will die and so presumably will many animals from the other seven arboreal marsupial species and numerous bird and bat species that live in this forest and rely on these same trees. (The other arboreal marsupials are the common ring-tail possum (*Pseudochirus pererinus*), mountain brushtail possum (*Trichosurus caninus*), common brushtail possum (*T. vulpecula*), greater glider (*Petauroides volans*), sugar glider (*Petaurus breviceps*), feathertail glider (*Acrobates pygmaeus*), and brush-tailed phascogale (*Phascogale tapoatafe*).) We have no idea how to address this looming catastrophe and, from our experience to date, it seems likely that the government agencies that are nominally responsible for managing wildlife will try very hard not to notice it. What is most evident is that the current strategies being used to address koala overabundance in other areas will be of no use whatsoever.

If we look back over the ecological history of the koala, as we related it in Chapter 2, we can see that there is ample evidence that koala populations were a valued food species that was harvested by the indigenous inhabitants of Australia for thousands for years. Prior to this koala numbers were probably controlled by a guild of mammalian, reptilian and possibly avian predators. With its poor soils, low productivity and low carrying capacity for herbivores Australia has not ever had the capacity to support many large carnivores, and this guild of koala predators were probably displaced when man arrived and took over their role. This ground has already been covered by Tim Flannery in his excellent book *The Future Eaters*. Suffice it to say that, following the demise of the indigenous hunters, the koala has had no significant predators and, in the south, there appears to be nothing that has regulated their abundance since. Given this scenario and looking forward to the problems of managing koalas in broad areas of rich habitat, such as on the Strathbogie Plateau, then what are our options? Because of the scale of the problem, the ones we have previously discussed will be of little use.

Australia is presently attempting to undergo a form of reconciliation with its Aboriginal people, the original inhabitants who were dispossessed and whose land was occupied under the pretext of *terra nullius*. As part of this process, don't we also need to embark on a reconciliation with the land itself and with its wildlife? Don't we need to shift our relationship, to move towards a more Aboriginal view of land and wildlife? Wildlife science has deepened our factual knowledge and taken us a part of the way, but science abhors spirituality and there is a substantial spiritual dimension to this. The animal welfare movement has tried to fill this role and has made some contribution. However, its more extreme proponents view it as having the authority of moral philosophy and it falls far short of this. It flounders badly when faced with the more difficult problems of living with wildlife: problems such as what action to take when a species is obviously overabundant.

In finding a way forward we can learn from the relationship that once existed between the Aboriginal people and the wildlife of this land. They knew the animals intimately, they revered them deeply and, with their stories and song lines, they passed this knowledge on to their children. Few of their stories are left now but, from the fragments that remain, we can see that the belief system of the original Australians was grounded in ecological reality. Koalas were not soft toys, nor were they baby surrogates. They were co-tenants of the land and of great spiritual significance. Yet, when necessary and according to the law, they could be utilised. Wouldn't it be far more humane, and vastly more sensible, for us to resume this practice?

REFERENCES AND FURTHER READING

CHAPTER 1

Milne AA, *Winnie-the-Pooh*, Methuen and Co., London, 146 pp., 1926

Pratt A, *The call of the koala*, Robertson and Mullens, Melbourne, 120 pp., 1937

Strahan R, *A dictionary of Australian mammal names*, Angus and Robertson, 196 pp., 1981

Strahan R and Martin RW, 'The koala: little fact, much emotion', pp 147–55 in Groves RH and Ride WDL (eds), *Species at Risk: Research in Australia*, Australian Academy of Science, Canberra, 1982

Wingrove K, *Norman Lindsay's Bears*, Macmillan, South Melbourne, 72 pp., 1978

CHAPTER 2

"An Old Bushman" (Wheelwright HW), *Bush wanderings of a naturalist*, Frederick Warne and Co,, London, 1865

Archer M, Hand SJ and Godthelp H, *Riversleigh: the story of animals in ancient rain-forests of inland Australia*, Reed Books, Sydney, 1991

Brough Smyth R, *The Aborigines of Victoria*, John Ferres, Government Printer, 1878

Campbell A, *Victorian Aborigines: John Bulmer's Recollections* 1855–1908, (Occasional Papers, Anthropology and History Series, no. 1), Museum of Victoria, 1994

Flannery TF, *The future eaters*, Reed Books, Sydney, 1994

Gould J, *The mammals of Australia*, Taylor and Francis, London, 1863

Govatt WR, 'Sketches of New South Wales No. XIV: On the animals called "monkeys" in New South Wales', *The Saturday Magazine*, 9, pp. 249–50, 1836

Iredale T and Whitley GP, 'The early history of the koala', *Victorian Naturalist*, 51, pp. 62–72, 1934

Kershaw JA, 'Excursion to National Park, Wilson's Promontory', *Victorian Naturalist*, 31, pp. 143–52, 1915

Le Souef WHD, *Wild life in Australia*, Whitcombe and Tombs, Christchurch NZ, 439 pp., 1922

Lunney D and Leary T, 'The impact on native mammals of land-use changes and exotic species in the Bega district, New South Wales, since settlement', *Australian Journal of Ecology*, 13, pp. 67–92, 1988

Lydekker R, *A handbook to the Marsupialia and Monotremata*, WH Allen and Co., , London, 1894

Mackaness G, *George Augustus Robinson's journey into south-eastern Australia, 1844*, privately printed, DS Ford, Sydney, 1941

Marshall AJ (ed.), *The great extermination: A guide to Anglo-Australian cupidity, wickedness and waste*, Heinemann, 1966

Massola A, *Bunjil's Cave: Myths, legends and superstitions of the Aborigines of south eastern Australia*, Landsdowne Press, 1968

Palmer N, *The Dandenongs*, The National Press, [1930s]

Parris HS, 'Koalas on the lower Goulburn', *Victorian Naturalist*, 64, pp. 192–93, 1948

Rawson G, *The Count: A life of Sir Paul Edmund Strzelecki, KCMG, explorer and scientist*, William Heinemann Ltd, 1953

Robinson R, *The Man Who Sold His Dreaming*, Currawong Publishing, Sydney, 1965

Troughton E, *Furred animals of Australia*, Angus and Robertson, Sydney, 1941

CHAPTER 3

Downes SJ, Handasyde KA and Elgar MA, 'The use of corridors by mammals in fragmented Australian eucalypt forests', *Conservation Biology*, 11, pp. 718–26, 1997

Gall BC, 'Aspects of the ecology of the koala *Phascolarctos cinereus* in Tucki Tucki Nature Reserve, New South Wales', *Australian Wildlife Research* 7, pp. 167–76, 1980

Gordon G, Brown AS and Pulsford T, 'A koala *Phascolarctos cinereus* Goldfuss population crash during drought and heatwave conditions in south-western Queensland', *Australian Journal of Ecology* 13, pp. 451–61, 1988

Hindell MA, 'The feeding ecology of the koala, *Phascolarctos cinereus*, in a mixed *Eucalyptus* forest', MSc thesis, Department of Zoology, Monash University, 1984

Martin RW and Handasyde KA, 'Koala' in Strahan R (ed.), *The mammals of Australia*, pp. 195–98, Australian Museum/Reed Books, Sydney, 1995

Melzer A and Lamb D, 'Low density populations of the koala *Phascolarctos cinereus* in Central Queensland', *Proceedings of the Royal Society of Queensland*, 104, pp. 89–93, 1994

Menkhorst P, (ed.), *Mammals of Victoria: Distribution, ecology and conservation*, Oxford University Press, Melbourne, 359 pp., 1995

Mitchell P and Martin RW, 'The structure and dynamics of koala populations: French Island in perspective', in Lee AK, Handasyde KA and Sanson GD (eds), *Biology of the Koala*, pp, 97–108, Surrey Beatty and Sons, Chipping Norton, 1991

Munks SA, Corkrey R and Foley WJ, 'Characteristics of arboreal marsupial habitat in the semi-arid woodlands of northern Queensland', *Wildlife Research*, 23, pp. 185–95, 1996

Phillips B, *The little Australian we'd all hate to lose*, Australian Government Publishing Service, Canberra, 1990

Somerville JD, 'The koalas western range', *Victorian Naturalist*, 54, p. 195, 1938

Troughton E le G, 'The southern race of the koala', *The Australian Naturalist*, 9, pp. 137–40, 1935

CHAPTER 4

Bednarik R, *Habitat use by koalas at the Koala Conservation Centre, Phillip Is*, hons thesis, Dept of Zoology, University of Melbourne, Victoria, 1996

Cork SJ, 'Utilisation of *Eucalyptus* foliage by arboreal marsupials', *Proceedings of the Nutritional Society of Australia*, 9, pp. 88–97, 1984

Cork SJ and Foley WJ, 'Digestive and metabolic strategies of arboreal mammalian folivores in relation to chemical defences in temperate and tropical forests' in Palo RT and Robbins CT (eds), *Plant defences against mammalian herbivory*, CRC Press, Boca Ralton, pp. 133–66, 1991

Cork SJ and Foley WJ, 'Digestion and metabolic adaptations of arboreal marsupials for dealing with plant antinutrients and toxins' in Saunders NR and Hinds LA (eds), *Marsupial biology: recent research, new perspectives*, University of New South Wales Press, Sydney, pp. 204–26, 1997

Cork SJ, Hume ID and Dawson TJ, 'Digestion and metabolism of a natural foliar diet *Eucalyptus punctata* by an arboreal marsupial, the koala *Phascolarctos cinereus*', *Journal of Comparative Physiology*, 153, pp. 181–90, 1983

Cork SJ and Sanson GD, 'Digestion and nutrition in the koala: a review in Lee AK, Handasyde KAand Sanson GD (eds), *Biology of the koala*, Surrey Beatty and Sons, Chipping Norton, NSW, pp. 129–44, 1991

Hindell MA and Lee AK, 'Tree use by individual koalas in a natural forest', *Australian Wildlife Research*, 15, pp. 1–7, 1988

Hindell MA, Handasye KA and Lee AK, 'Tree species selection by free-ranging koala populations in Victoria', *Australian Wildlife Research*, 12, pp. 137–44, 1985

Hume ID, *Marsupial nutrition*, Cambridge University Press, Cambridge, 1999

Krockenberger AK, 'Energetics and nutrition during reproduction in the koala', PhD thesis, University of Sydney, 1993

Krockenberger AK, Hume ID and Cork SJ, 'Production of milk and nutrition of dependent young of free-ranging koalas *Phascolarctos cinereusi*', *Physiological Zoology*, 71, pp. 45–56, 1998

Lanyon JM and Sanson GD, 'Koala *Phascolarctos cinereus* dentition and nutrition II: Implications of tooth wear and nutrition', *Journal of Zoology*, 209, pp. 169–81, 1986

Lawler IR, Foley WJ, Eschler B, Pass DM and Handasyde KA, 'Intraspecific variation in *Eucalyptus* secondary metabolites determines food intake by folivorous marsupials', *Oecologia*, 116, pp. 160–69, 1998

McArthur C, Hagerman AE and Robbins CT, 'Physiological strategies of mammalian herbivores against plant defences' in Palo RT and Robbins CT (eds), *Plant defences against mammalian herbivory*, CRC Press Boca Ralton, pp. 103–14, 1991

Mezler A and Lamb D, 'Low density populations of the koala *Phascolarctos cinereus* in central Queensland', *Proceedings of the Royal Society of Queensland*, 104, pp. 89–93, 1994

Mitchell P, 'The home ranges and social activity of koalas: a quantitative analysis', pp 171–87 in Lee AK, Handasyde KA and Sanson GD (eds), *Biology of the koala*, Surrey Beatty and Sons, Chipping Norton NSW, 1991

Nagy KA and Martin RW, 'Field metabolic rate water flux food consumption and time budget of koalas *Phascolarctos cinereus* Marsupialia: Phacolarctidae in Victoria', *Australian Journal of Zoology*, 33, pp. 655–65, 1985

Nagy KA, 'Field metabolic rate and food requirement scaling in mammals and birds', *Ecological Monographs*, 57, pp. 111–28, 1987

Pahl LI and Hume ID, 'Preferences for *Eucalyptus* species of the New England Tablelands and initial development of an artificial diet for koalas', pp. 123–28 in Lee AK, Handasyde KA and Sanson GD (eds), *Biology of the koala*, Surrey Beatty and Sons, Chipping Norton NSW, 1991

Reed PC, Lunney D and Walker P, 'A 1986–87 survey of the koala *Phascolarctos cinereus* Goldfuss in New South Wales and an ecological interpretation of its distribution', pp. 55–74 in Lee AK, Handasyde KA and Sanson GD (eds), *Biology of the koala*, Surrey Beatty and Sons, Chipping Norton NSW, 1991

Stevens CE and Hume ID, *Comparative physiology of the vertebrate digestive system*, 2nd ed, Cambridge University Press, Cambridge, 1995

Warneke RM, 'The status of the koala in Victoria', pp. 109–14 in Bergin TJ (ed.), *The koala*, Zoological Parks Board of New South Wales, Sydney, 1978

White NA and Kunst ND, 'Aspects of the ecology of the koala in southern Queensland', pp. 109–16 in Lee AK, Handasyde KA and Sanson GD (eds), *Biology of the koala*, Surrey Beatty and Sons, Chipping Norton NSW, 1991

CHAPTER 5

Blanshard WH 'Growth and development of the koala from birth to weaning', pp. 193–202 in Lee AK, Handasyde KA and Sanson GD (eds), *Biology of the koala*, Surrey Beatty and Sons, Chipping Norton NSW, 1991

Eberhard IH, 'Ecology of the koala *Phascolarctos cinereus* Goldfuss Marsupialia: Phascolarctidae in Australia', pp. 315–27 in Gene Montgomery G (ed.), *The ecology of arboreal folivores*, Smithsonian Institution Press, Washington DC, 1978

Flannery TF, *The future eaters*, Reed Books, Sydney, 1996

Haight JR and Nelson JE, 'A brain that doesn't fit its skull: a comparative study of the brain and endocranium of the koala *Phascolarctos cinereus* Marsupialia: Phascolarctidae', pp. 331–52 in Archer M (ed.), *Possums and opossums: studies in evolution*, Surrey Beatty and Sons/Royal Zoological Society of New South Wales, Sydney, 1987

Handasyde KA, McDonald IR, Than KA, Michaelides J and Martin RW, 'Reproductive hormones and reproduction in the koala', pp. 203–10 in Lee AK, Handasyde KA and Sanson GD (eds), *Biology of the koala*, Surrey Beatty and Sons, Chipping Norton NSW, 1991

Jones FW and Porteus SD, 'The matrix of the mind', Edward Arnold, London, 1929

Krockenberger AK, 'Composition of the milk of the koala *Phascolarctos cinereus an arboreal folivore*', *Physiological Zoology*, 69, pp. 701–18, 1996

Krockenberger AK, Hume ID and Cork SJ, 'Production of milk and nutrition of dependent young of free-ranging koalas *Phascolarctos cinereus*', *Physiological Zoology*, 71, pp. 45–56, 1998

Lee AK Martin RW and Handasyde KA, 'Experimental translocation of koalas to new habitat', pp. 299–312 in in Lee AK, Handasyde KA and Sanson GD (eds), *Biology of the koala*, Surrey Beatty and Sons, Chipping Norton NSW, 1991

Marshall V, Carrick F, Doherty MD and Maclean DJ, 'Aspects of the composition of koala milk', pp. 229–41 in in Lee AK, Handasyde KA and Sanson GD (eds), *Biology of the koala*, Surrey Beatty and Sons, Chipping Norton NSW, 1991

Martin RW, 'Age specific fertility in three populations of the koala *Phascolarctos cinereus* Goldfuss in Victoria', *Australian Wildlife Research*, 8, pp. 278–83, 1981.

Martin RW and Handasyde KA, 'Population dynamics of the koala *Phascolarctos cinereus* in south-eastern Australia', pp. 75–84 in in Lee AK, Handasyde KA and Sanson GD (eds), *Biology of the koala*, Surrey Beatty and Sons, Chipping Norton NSW, 1991

Martin RW and Handasyde KA, 'Koala', pp. 195–98 in Strahan R (ed.), *The mammals of Australia*, Australian Museum/Reed Books, Sydney, 1995

Milne AA, *The house at Pooh Corner*, Methuen and Co., London, 1928

Minchin K, 'Notes on the weaning of a young koala *Phascolarctos cinereus*', *Records of the South Australian Museum*, 6, pp. 1–3, 1937

Mitchell PJ, 'Social behaviour and communication of koalas', pp. 151–70 in Lee AK, Handasyde KA and Sanson GD (eds), *Biology of the koala*, Surrey Beatty and Sons, Chipping Norton NSW, 1991

Mitchell PJ, 'The home range and social activity of koalas: a quantitative analysis', pp. 171–87 in Lee AK, Handasyde KA and Sanson GD (eds), *Biology of the koala*, Surrey Beatty and Sons, Chipping Norton NSW, 1991

Mitchell PJ and Martin RW, 'The structure and dynamics of koala populations - French

Island in perspective', pp. 97–108 in Lee AK, Handasyde KA and Sanson GD (eds), *Biology of the koala*, Surrey Beatty and Sons, Chipping Norton NSW, 1991

Osawa R, Blanshard WH and O'Callaghan PG, 'Microbial studies of the intestinal microflora of the koala *Phascolarctos cinereus* II: Pap a special maternal faeces consumed by juvenile koalas', *Australian Journal of Zoology*, 41, pp. 611–20, 1993

Pratt A, *The call of the koala*, Robertson and Mullens, Melbourne, 1937

Sharpe LL, 'Behaviour of the koala *Phascolarctos cinereus*',hons thesis, Monash University, Clayton, Victoria, 1980

Thompson VD, 'Parturition and development in the Queensland koala *Phascolarctos cinereus adjustus* at San Diego Zoo', *International Zoo Yearbook*, 26, pp. 217–22, 1987

CHAPTER 6

Blanshard WH, 'Medicine and husbandry of koalas', pp. 547–626 in *Wildlife: the TG Hungerford Refresher Course for Veterinarians, Proceedings* 233, Post Graduate Committee in Veterinary Science, University of Sydney, 1994

Brown AS and Grice RG, 'Isolation of *Chlamydia psittaci* from koalas *Phascolarctos cinereus*', *Australian Veterinary Journal*, 61, p. 413, 1984

Canfield PJ, Brown AS, Kelley WR and Sutton RH, 'Spontaneous lymphoid neoplasia in the koala *Phascolarctos cinereus*', *Journal of Comparative Pathology*, 97, pp. 171–78, 1987

Canfield PJ, 'Disease studies on New South Wales koalas', pp. 249–54 in Lee AK, Handasyde KA and Sanson GD (eds), *Biology of the koala*, Surrey Beatty and Sons, Chipping Norton NSW, 1991

Cockram FA and Jackson ARB, 'Isolation of a *Chlamydia* from cases of keratoconjunctivitis in the koala', *Australian Veterinary Journal*, 50, pp. 82–83, 1974

Glasick T, Giffard P and Timms P, 'Outer protein 2 gene sequences indicate that *Chlamydia pecorum* and *Chlamydia pneumoniae* cause infections in koalas', *Systematic and Applied Microbiology*, 1997

Handasyde KA, Martin RW and Lee AK, 'Field investigations into Chlamydial disease and infertility in koalas in Victoria', pp. 505–15 in *Australian Wildlife Proceedings* 104, Post-graduate Committee in Veterinary Science, University of Sydney, NSW, 1988

Lavin MF, Girjes AA, Hugall AF, Timms P, Weigler BJ and Brown S, '*Chlamydia psittaci* and disease in *Phascolarctos cinereus* koala', pp. 261–66 in Lee AK, Handasyde KA and Sanson GD (eds), *Biology of the koala*, Surrey Beatty and Sons, Chipping Norton NSW, 1991

Lee AK, Martin RW and Handasyde KA, 'Experimental translocation of koalas into new habitat', pp. 299–312 in Lee AK, Handasyde KA and Sanson GD (eds), *Biology of the koala*, Surrey Beatty and Sons, Chipping Norton NSW, 1991

McColl KA, Martin RW, Gleeson LJ, Handasyde KA and Lee AK, '*Chlamydia* infection and infertility in the female koala *Phascolarctos cinereus*', *Veterinary Record*, 115, p. 655, 1984

Martin RW, 'Age-specific fertility in three populations of the koala *Phascolarctus cinereus* Goldfuss in Victoria', *Australian Wildlife Research*, 8, pp. 275–83, 1981

Obendorf DL, 'Pathology of the female reproductive tract in the koala *Phascolarctos cinereus* Goldfuss from Victoria Australia', *Journal of Wildlife Diseases*, 17, pp. 587–92, 1981

Timms P, Eaves FW, Girges AA and Lavin MF, 'Comparison of *Chlamydia psittaci* isolates by restriction endonuclease and DNA probe analysis', *Infection and Immunity*, 56, pp. 287–90, 1988

Weigler BJ, Girges AA, White NA, Kunst ND, Carrick FN and Lavin MF, 'Aspects of the epidemiology of *Chlamydia Psittaci* infection in a population of koalas *Phascolarctos cinereus* in southeastern Queensland Australia', *Journal of Wildlife Diseases*, 24, pp. 282–91, 1988

CHAPTER 7

Braithwaite RW, Lumsden LF and Dixon JM 'A short history of Quail Island', pp. 44–48 in *Sites of zoological significance in the Western Port region: interim report top of the bay area*, National Museum Victoria, 1980

Gordon G, Brown AS and Pulsford T, 'A koala *Phascolarctos cinereus* Goldfuss population crash during drought and heatwave conditions in south-western Queensland', *Australian Journal of Ecology*, 13, pp. 451–61, 1988

Gordon G, McGreevy DG and Lawrie BC, 'Koala populations in Queensland: major limiting factors', pp. 85–95 in Lee AK, Handasyde KA and Sanson GD (eds), *Biology of the koala*, Surrey Beatty and Sons, Chipping Norton NSW, 1991

Kemp DH, 'John Leadbeater 1831–88: a naturalist in Victoria', *Victorian Historical Journal*, February, 1979

Martin RW and Handasyde KA, 'Population dynamics of the koala *Phascolarctos cinereus* in south-eastern Australia', pp. 75–84 in Lee AK, Handasyde KA and Sanson GD (eds), *Biology of the koala*, Surrey Beatty and Sons, Chipping Norton NSW, 1991

Mitchell P and Martin RW, 'The structure and dynamics of koala populations: French Island in perspective', pp. 97–108 in Lee AK, Handasyde KA and Sanson GD (eds), *Biology of the koala*, Surrey Beatty and Sons, Chipping Norton NSW, 1991

Weigler BJ, Girges AA, White NA, Kunst ND, Carrick FN and Lavin MF, 'Aspects of the epidemiology of *Chlamydia psittaci* infection in a population of koalas *Phascolarctos cinereus* in southeastern Queensland Australia', *Journal of Wildlife Diseases*, 24, pp. 282–91, 1988

White NA and Kunst ND, 'Aspects of the ecology of the koala in southern Queensland',pp. 109–16 in Lee AK, Handasyde KA and Sanson GD (eds), *Biology of the koala*, Surrey Beatty and Sons, Chipping Norton NSW, 1991

CHAPTER 8

Downes SJ, Handasyde KA and Elgar MA, 'The use of corridors by mammals in fragmented Australian eucalypt forests', *Conservation Biology*, 11, pp. 718–26, 1997

Houlden BA, England PR, Taylor AC, Greville WD and Sherwin WB, 'Low genetic variability of the koala *Phascolarcto cinereus* in south- eastern Australia following a severe bottleneck', *Molecular Ecology*, 5, pp. 269–81, 1996

McNally J, 'A field survey of a koala population', *Proceedings of the Royal Society of NSW 1955–56*, pp. 18–27, 1957

Malthus TR, *An essay on the principles of population: or a view of its past and present effects on human happiness with an inquiry into our prospects respecting the future removal or mitigation of the evils which it occasions*, 6th ed, 2 vols, Murray, 1826

Martin RW, 'Managing over-abundance in koala populations in south-eastern Australia: future options', *Australian Biologist*, 10, 1, pp. 57–63, 1997

Munks SA, Corkrey R and Foley WJ, 'Characteristics of arboreal marsupial habitat in the semi-arid woodlands of northern Queensland', *Wildlife Research*, 23, pp. 185–95, 1996

Possingham H, Barton M, Boxall M, Dunstan J, Gibbs J, Greig J, Inns B, Munday B, Paton D, Vickery F, and St John B, *Koala Management Task Force: final report*, Dept of Environmental Science and Management, University of Adelaide, 1996

St John B, 'Risk assessment and koala management in South Australia', *Australian Biologist*, 10, 1, pp. 47–56, 1997

Taylor AC, Graves JM, Murray ND, OBrien SJ, Yuhki N and Sherwin WB, 'Conservation genetics of the koala *Phascolarcto cinereus*: low mitochondrial DNA variation amongst southern Australian populations', *Genetical Research*, 69, pp. 25–33, Cambridge, 1997

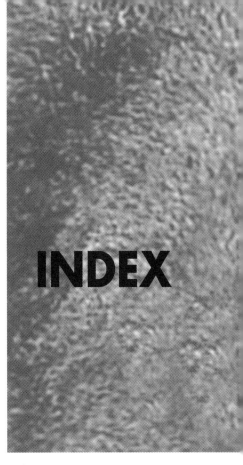

INDEX

Page numbers in **bold** refer to illustrations or diagrams; plates refer to colour plates.